Succeed

Eureka Math®
Grade 4
Modules 4–5

TEKS EDITION

Great Minds® is the creator of *Eureka Math*®, *Wit & Wisdom*®, *Alexandria Plan*™, and *PhD Science*®.

Published by Great Minds PBC.
greatminds.org

Copyright © 2021 Great Minds PBC. Except where otherwise noted, this content is published under a limited public license with the Texas Education Agency. Use limited to Non-Commercial educational purposes. For more information, visit https://gm.greatminds.org/texas.

Printed in the USA
1 2 3 4 5 6 7 8 9 10 BAB 25 24 23 22 21

ISBN 978-1-64929-686-3

Learn ♦ Practice ♦ Succeed

Eureka Math® student materials for *A Story of Units®* (K–5) are available in the *Learn, Practice, Succeed* trio. This series supports differentiation and remediation while keeping student materials organized and accessible. Educators will find that the *Learn, Practice,* and *Succeed* series also offers coherent—and therefore, more effective—resources for Response to Intervention (RTI), extra practice, and summer learning.

Learn

Eureka Math Learn serves as a student's in-class companion where they show their thinking, share what they know, and watch their knowledge build every day. *Learn* assembles the daily classwork—Application Problems, Exit Tickets, Problem Sets, templates—in an easily stored and navigated volume.

Practice

Each *Eureka Math* lesson begins with a series of energetic, joyous fluency activities, including those found in *Eureka Math Practice.* Students who are fluent in their math facts can master more material more deeply. With *Practice,* students build competence in newly acquired skills and reinforce previous learning in preparation for the next lesson.

Together, *Learn* and *Practice* provide all the print materials students will use for their core math instruction.

Succeed

Eureka Math Succeed enables students to work individually toward mastery. These additional problem sets align lesson by lesson with classroom instruction, making them ideal for use as homework or extra practice. Each problem set is accompanied by a Homework Helper, a set of worked examples that illustrate how to solve similar problems.

Teachers and tutors can use *Succeed* books from prior grade levels as curriculum-consistent tools for filling gaps in foundational knowledge. Students will thrive and progress more quickly as familiar models facilitate connections to their current grade-level content.

Students, families, and educators:

Thank you for being part of the *Eureka Math*® community, where we celebrate the joy, wonder, and thrill of mathematics.

Nothing beats the satisfaction of success—the more competent students become, the greater their motivation and engagement. The *Eureka Math Succeed* book provides the guidance and extra practice students need to shore up foundational knowledge and build mastery with new material.

What is in the Succeed *book?*

Eureka Math Succeed books deliver supported practice sets that parallel the lessons of *A Story of Units*®. Each *Succeed* lesson begins with a set of worked examples, called *Homework Helpers*, that illustrate the modeling and reasoning the curriculum uses to build understanding. Next, students receive scaffolded practice through a series of problems carefully sequenced to begin from a place of confidence and add incremental complexity.

How should Succeed *be used?*

The collection of *Succeed* books can be used as differentiated instruction, practice, homework, or intervention. When coupled with *Affirm*®, *Eureka Math*'s digital assessment system, *Succeed* lessons enable educators to give targeted practice and to assess student progress. *Succeed*'s perfect alignment with the mathematical models and language used across *A Story of Units* ensures that students feel the connections and relevance to their daily instruction, whether they are working on foundational skills or getting extra practice on the current topic.

Where can I learn more about Eureka Math *resources?*

The Great Minds® team is committed to supporting students, families, and educators with an ever-growing library of resources, available at eureka-math.org. The website also offers inspiring stories of success in the *Eureka Math* community. Share your insights and accomplishments with fellow users by becoming a *Eureka Math* Champion.

Best wishes for a year filled with Eureka moments!

Jill Diniz
Jill Diniz
Director of Mathematics
Great Minds

Contents

Module 4: Angle Measure and Plane Figures

Topic A: Lines and Angles
Lesson 1 3
Lesson 2 7
Lesson 3 13
Lesson 4 19

Topic B: Angle Measurement
Lesson 5 25
Lesson 6 29
Lesson 7 35
Lesson 8 39

Topic C: Problem Solving with the Addition of Angle Measures
Lesson 9 43
Lesson 10 47
Lesson 11 51

Topic D: Two-Dimensional Figures and Symmetry
Lesson 12 57
Lesson 13 61
Lesson 14 65
Lesson 15 69
Lesson 16 73

Module 5: Fraction Equivalence, Ordering, and Operations

Topic A: Decomposition and Fraction Equivalence
Lesson 1 79
Lesson 2 83
Lesson 3 87

Lesson 4 93

Lesson 5 97

Topic B: Fraction Equivalence Using Multiplication and Division

Lesson 6 103

Lesson 7 107

Lesson 8 111

Lesson 9 117

Lesson 10 123

Topic C: Fraction Comparison

Lesson 11 129

Lesson 12 133

Lesson 13 137

Lesson 14 143

Topic D: Fraction Addition and Subtraction

Lesson 15 149

Lesson 16 153

Lesson 17 157

Lesson 18 161

Topic E: Extending Fraction Equivalence to Fractions Greater Than 1

Lesson 19 165

Lesson 20 169

Lesson 21 173

Lesson 22 177

Lesson 23 181

Lesson 24 185

Topic F: Addition and Subtraction of Fractions by Decomposition

Lesson 25 189

Lesson 26 193

Lesson 27 199

Lesson 28 203

Lesson 29 207

Lesson 30 211

Lesson 31 215

Grade 4
Module 4

A STORY OF UNITS – TEKS EDITION   Lesson 1 Homework Helper 4•4

1. Use the following directions to draw a figure in the box below.
   a. Draw two points: J and K.
   b. Use a straightedge to draw $\overleftrightarrow{JK}$. — I read this as "line JK."
   c. Draw a new point that is on $\overleftrightarrow{JK}$. Label it L.
   d. Draw a point not on $\overleftrightarrow{JK}$. Label it M.
   e. Construct $\overline{LM}$. — I read this as "line segment LM."
   f. Use the points you've already labeled to name two angles.   ∠JLM, ∠MLK
   g. Identify the angles you've labeled by drawing an arc to indicate the position of the angles.

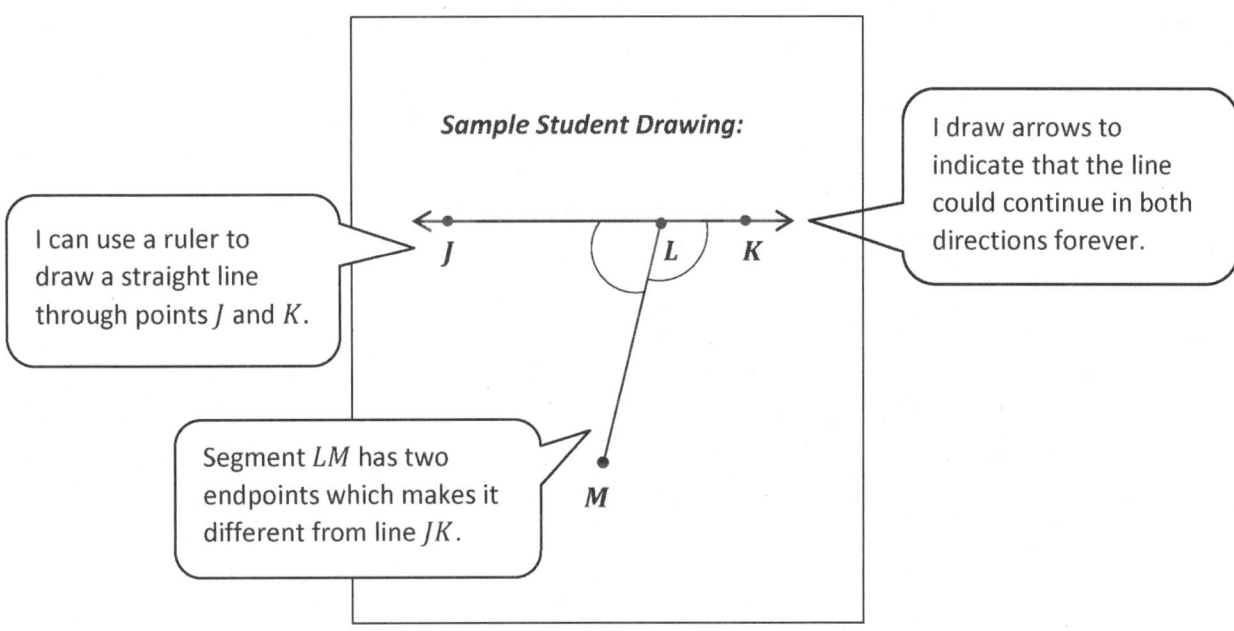

Lesson 1: Identify and draw points, lines, line segments, rays, and angles. Recognize them in various contexts and familiar figures.

2.
   a. Observe the familiar figures below. Label some points on each figure.
   b. Use those points to label and name representations of each of the following in the table below: ray, line, line segment, and angle. Extend segments to show lines and rays.

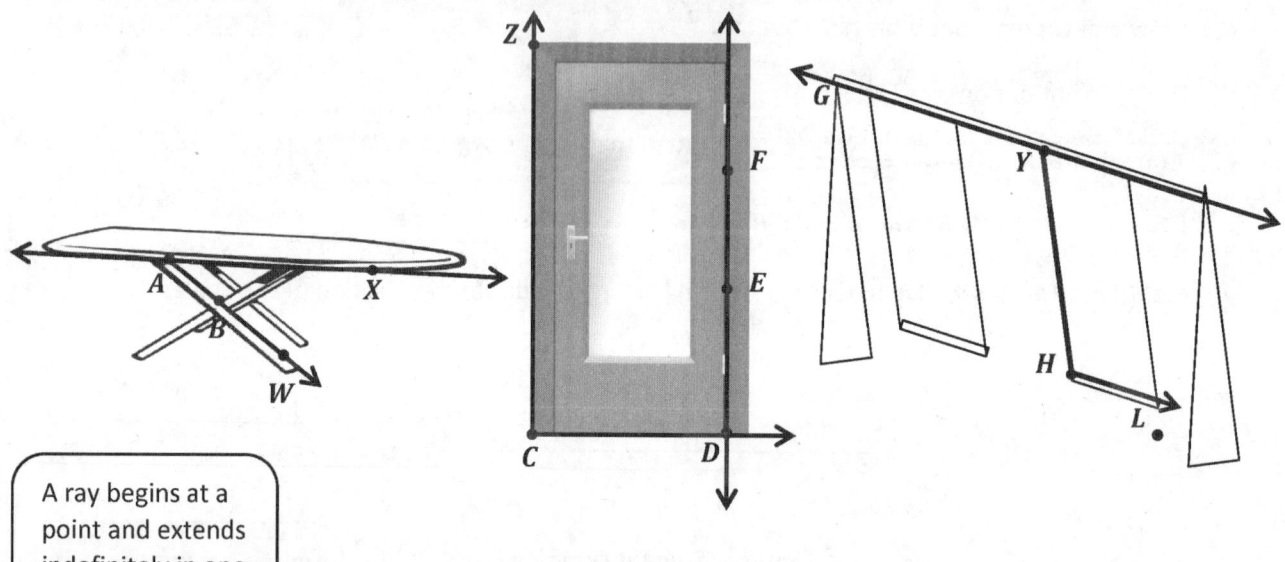

A ray begins at a point and extends indefinitely in one direction.

	Ironing Board	Door	Swing Set
Ray	$\overrightarrow{AW}$	$\overrightarrow{CD}$	$\overrightarrow{HL}$
Line	$\overleftrightarrow{AX}$	$\overleftrightarrow{DF}$	$\overleftrightarrow{GY}$
Line Segment	$\overline{AB}$	$\overline{EF}$	$\overline{YH}$
Angle	$\angle WAX$	$\angle ZCD$	$\angle YHL$

I write symbols for angle ($\angle$), segment ($\overline{}$), ray ($\overrightarrow{}$), and line ($\overleftrightarrow{}$).

Lesson 1: Identify and draw points, lines, line segments, rays, and angles. Recognize them in various contexts and familiar figures.

A STORY OF UNITS – TEKS EDITION Lesson 1 Homework 4•4

Name _____ Date _____

1. Use the following directions to draw a figure in the box to the right.

   a. Draw two points: W and X.
   b. Use a straightedge to draw $\overrightarrow{WX}$.
   c. Draw a new point that is not on $\overrightarrow{WX}$. Label it Y.
   d. Draw $\overline{WY}$.
   e. Draw a point not on $\overrightarrow{WX}$ or $\overline{WY}$. Call it Z.
   f. Construct $\overleftrightarrow{YZ}$.
   g. Use the points you've already labeled to name one angle. _____

2. Use the following directions to draw a figure in the box to the right.

   a. Draw two points: W and X.
   b. Use a straightedge to draw $\overline{WX}$.
   c. Draw a new point that is not on $\overline{WX}$. Label it Y.
   d. Draw $\overline{WY}$.
   e. Draw a new point that is not on $\overrightarrow{WY}$ or on the line containing $\overline{WX}$. Label it Z.
   f. Construct $\overleftrightarrow{WZ}$.
   g. Identify ∠ZWX by drawing an arc to indicate the position of the angle.
   h. Identify another angle by referencing points that you have already drawn. _____

Lesson 1: Identify and draw points, lines, line segments, rays, and angles.
 Recognize them in various contexts and familiar figures.

5

3. a. Observe the familiar figures below. Label some points on each figure.

   b. Use those points to label and name representations of each of the following in the table below: ray, line, line segment, and angle. Extend segments to show lines and rays.

  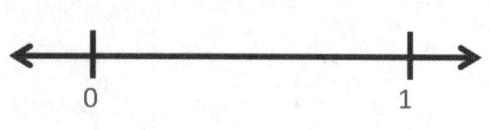

	Clock	Die	Number line
Ray			
Line			
Line segment			
Angle			

Extension: Draw a familiar figure. Label it with points, and then identify rays, lines, line segments, and angles as applicable.

A STORY OF UNITS – TEKS EDITION
Lesson 2 Homework Helper 4•4

> I can remake a right angle template using a circle of paper. I fold it into fourths and use the square corner.

1. Use the right angle template that you made in class to determine if each of the following angles is greater than, less than, or equal to a right angle. Label each as *greater than, less than,* or *equal to,* and then connect each angle to the correct label of acute, right, or obtuse.

> I draw a line to "acute" because it names this angle that is less than a right angle.

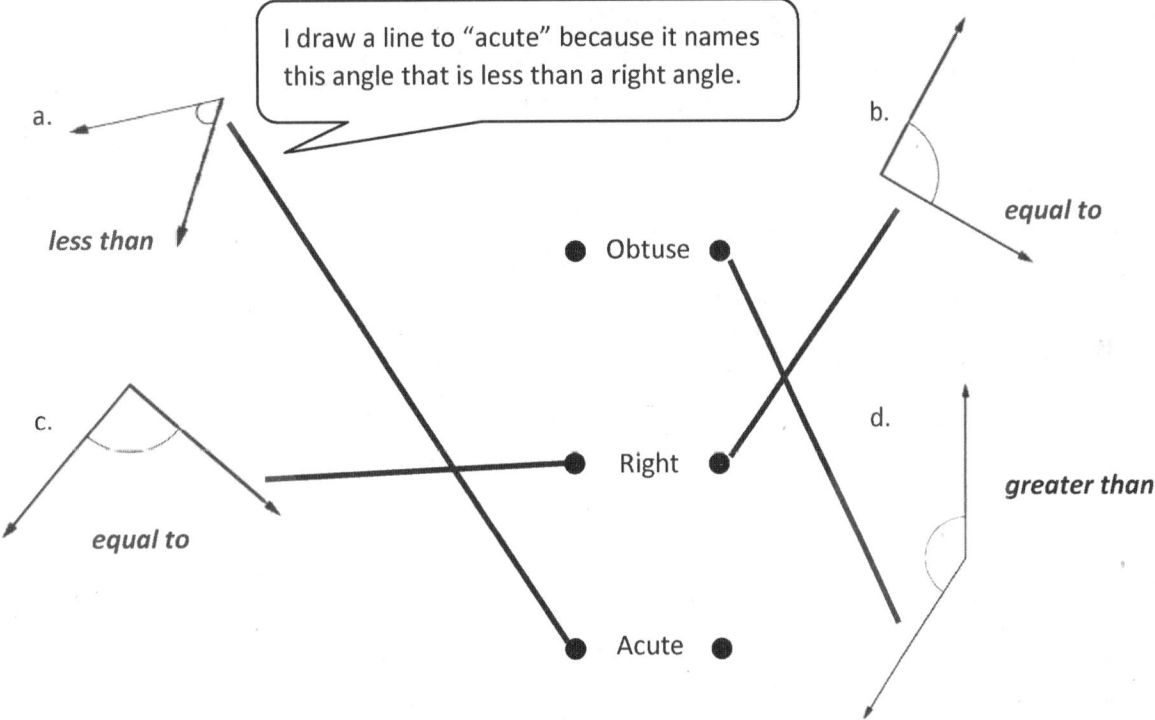

a. *less than*
b. *equal to*
c. *equal to*
d. *greater than*

2. Construct an obtuse angle using a straightedge and the right angle template that you created. Explain the characteristics of an obtuse angle by comparing it to a right angle. Use the words *greater than, less than,* or *equal to* in your explanation.

Sample explanation:

The measure of an obtuse angle is greater than the measure of a right angle.

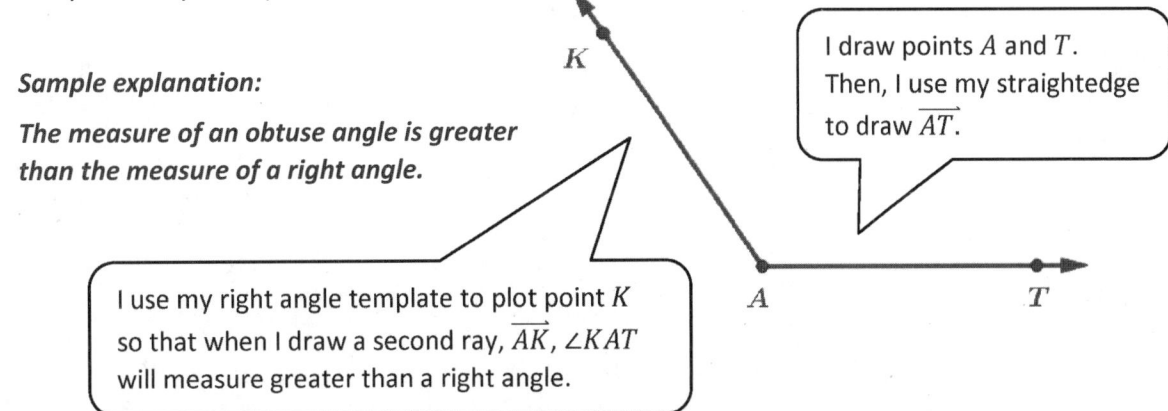

> I draw points A and T. Then, I use my straightedge to draw $\overrightarrow{AT}$.

> I use my right angle template to plot point K so that when I draw a second ray, $\overrightarrow{AK}$, $\angle KAT$ will measure greater than a right angle.

Lesson 2: Use right angles to determine whether angles are equal to, greater than, or less than right angles. Draw right, obtuse, and acute angles.

7

A STORY OF UNITS – TEKS EDITION

Lesson 2 Homework 4•4

Name _____ Date _____

1. Use the right angle template that you made in class to determine if each of the following angles is greater than, less than, or equal to a right angle. Label each as *greater than, less than*, or *equal to,* and then connect each angle to the correct label of acute, right, or obtuse. The first one has been completed for you.

a.

Less than

b.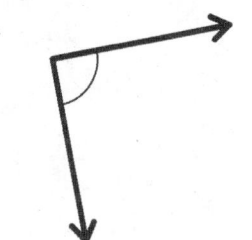

c.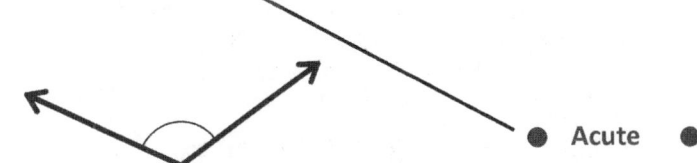

d.

● Acute ●

e.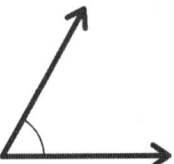

f.

● Right ●

g.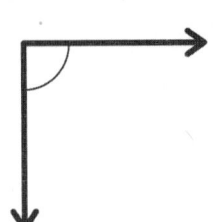

● Obtuse ●

h.

i.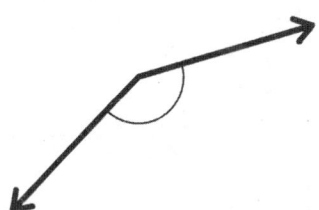

j.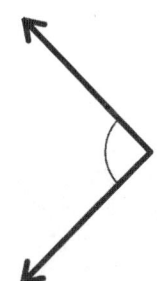

Lesson 2: Use right angles to determine whether angles are equal to, greater than, or less than right angles. Draw right, obtuse, and acute angles.

2. Use your right angle template to identify acute, obtuse, and right angles within this painting. Trace at least two of each, label with points, and then name them in the table below the painting.

Acute angle		
Obtuse angle		
Right angle		

3. Construct each of the following using a straightedge and the right angle template that you created. Explain the characteristics of each by comparing the angle to a right angle. Use the words *greater than*, *less than*, or *equal to* in your explanations.

   a. Acute angle

   b. Right angle

   c. Obtuse angle

A STORY OF UNITS – TEKS EDITION

Lesson 3 Homework Helper 4•4

1. On each object, trace at least one pair of lines that appear to be perpendicular.

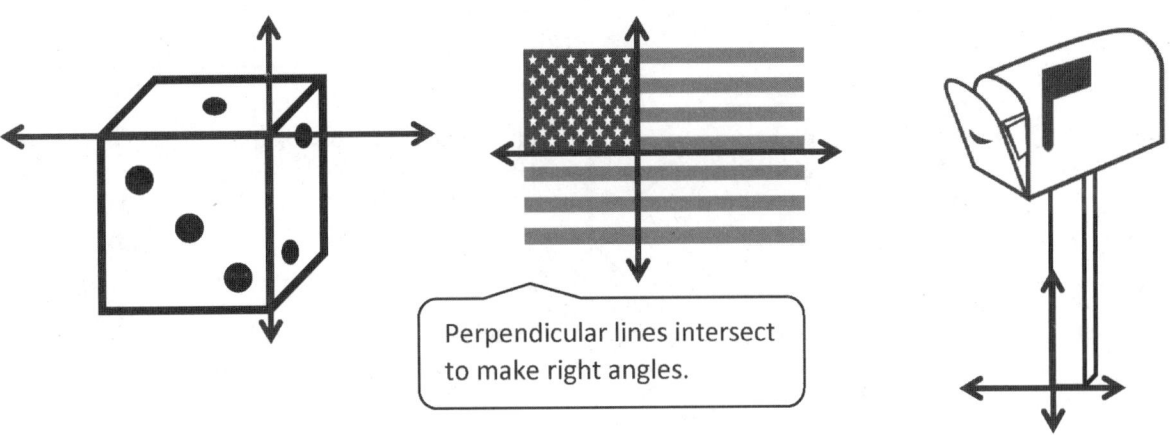

Perpendicular lines intersect to make right angles.

2. In the grid below, draw a segment that is perpendicular to the given segment. Use a straightedge.

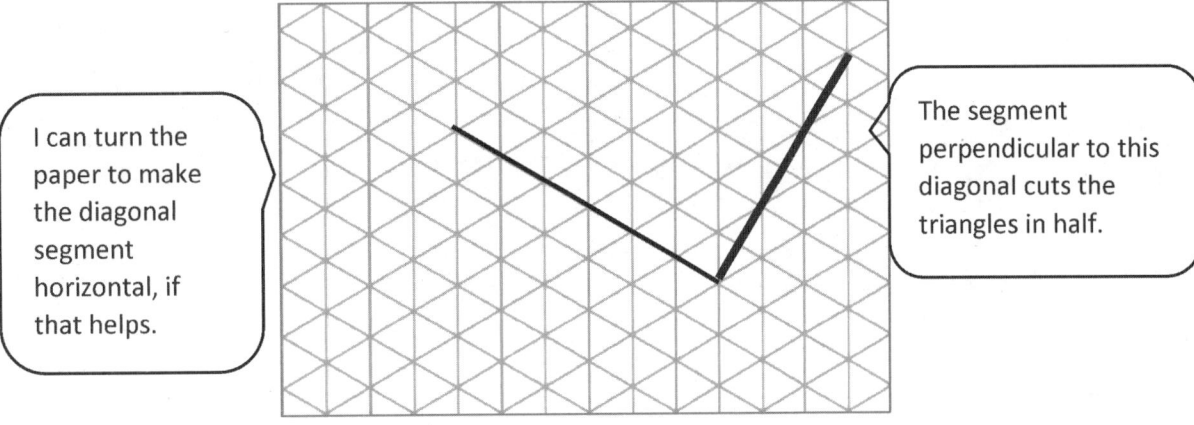

I can turn the paper to make the diagonal segment horizontal, if that helps.

The segment perpendicular to this diagonal cuts the triangles in half.

Lesson 3: Identify, define, and draw perpendicular lines.

3. Use the right angle template that you created in class to determine if the following figure has a right angle. If so, mark it with a small square. For each right angle you find, name the corresponding perpendicular sides.

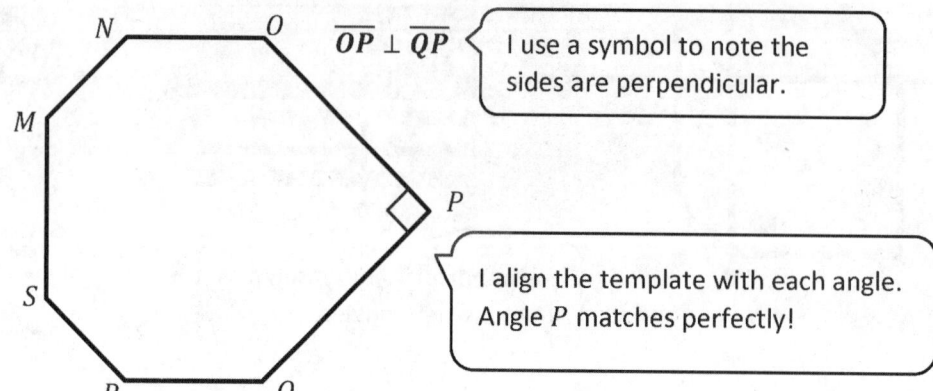

A STORY OF UNITS – TEKS EDITION   Lesson 3 Homework 4•4

Name _____   Date _____

1. On each object, trace at least one pair of lines that appear to be perpendicular.

2. How do you know if two lines are perpendicular?

3. In the square and triangular grids below, use the given segments in each grid to draw a segment that is perpendicular. Use a straightedge.

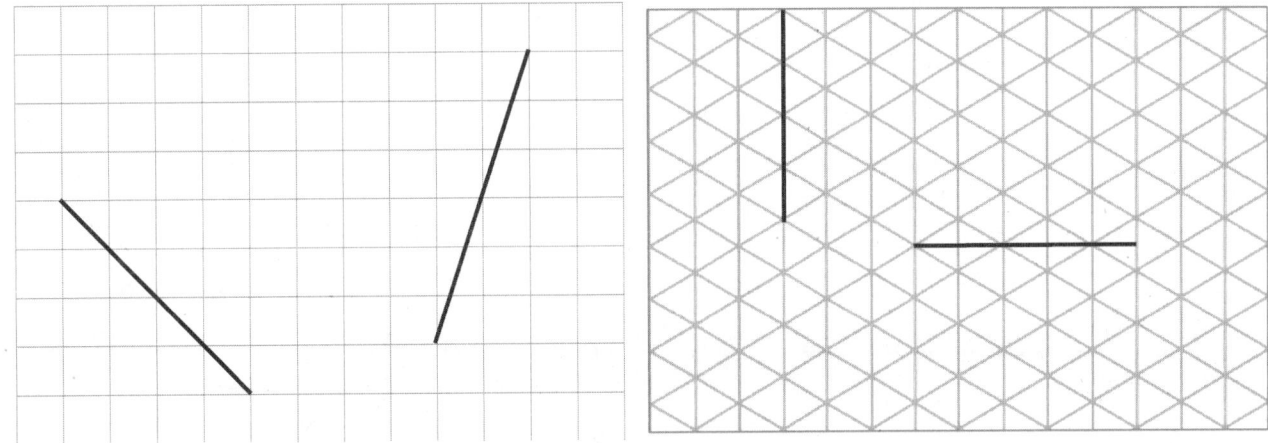

Lesson 3: Identify, define, and draw perpendicular lines.

15

4. Use the right angle template that you created in class to determine which of the following figures have a right angle. Mark each right angle with a small square. For each right angle you find, name the corresponding pair of perpendicular sides. (Problem 4(a) has been started for you.)

a. 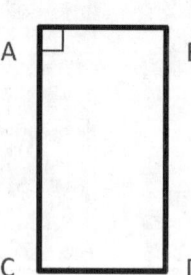 $\overline{CA} \perp \overline{AB}$

b.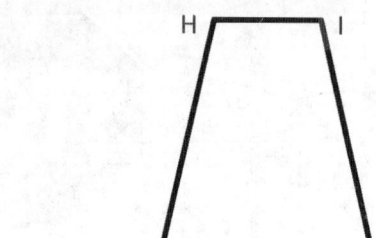

c.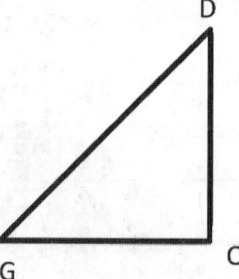

d.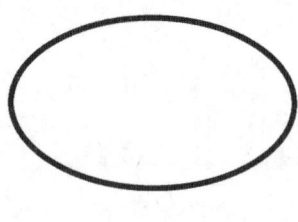

e.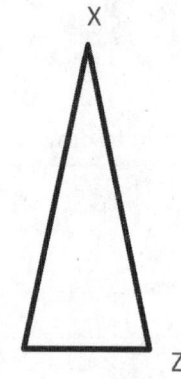

f.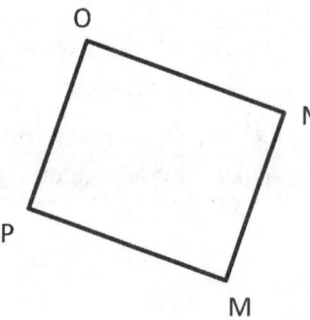

g.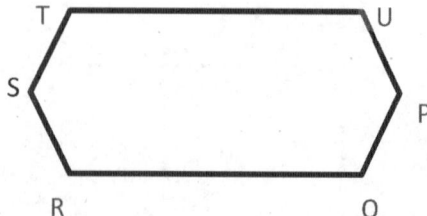

h.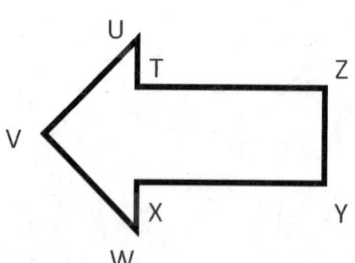

5. Use your right angle template as a guide, and mark each right angle in the following figure with a small square. (Note: A right angle does not have to be inside the figure.) How many pairs of perpendicular sides does this figure have?

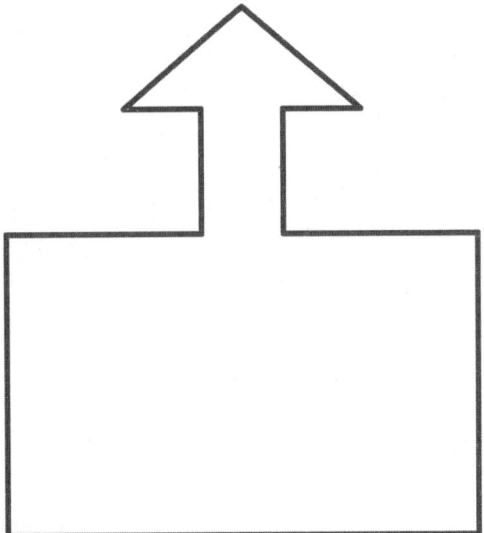

6. True or false? Shapes that have no right angles also have no perpendicular segments. Draw some figures to help explain your thinking.

On each object, trace at least one pair of lines that appear to be parallel.

1.

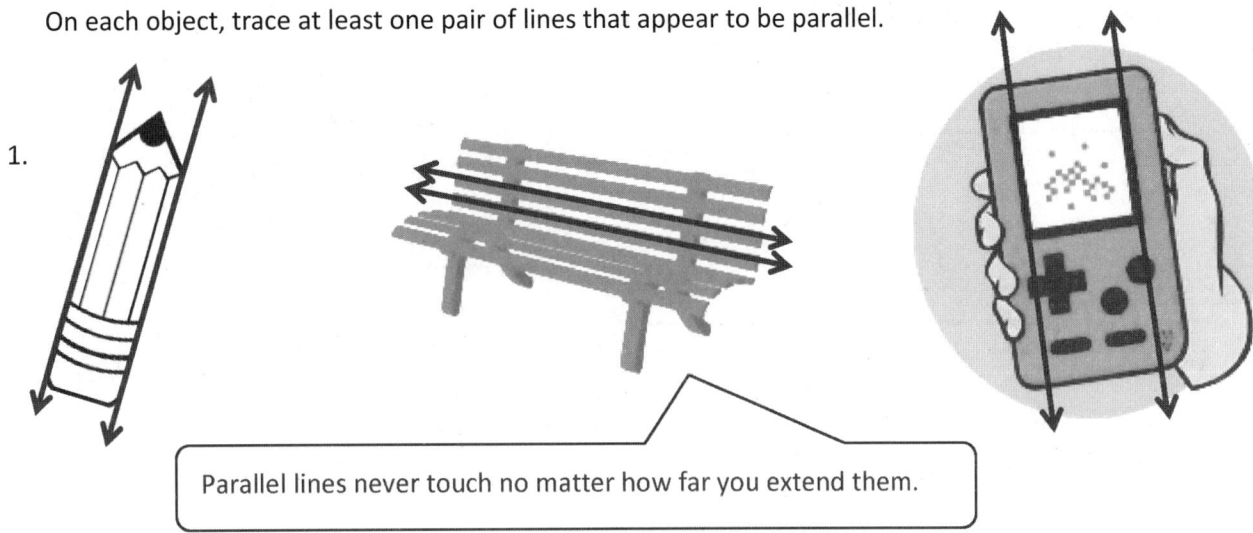

Parallel lines never touch no matter how far you extend them.

In the grid below, use a straightedge to draw a segment that is parallel to the given segment.

2.

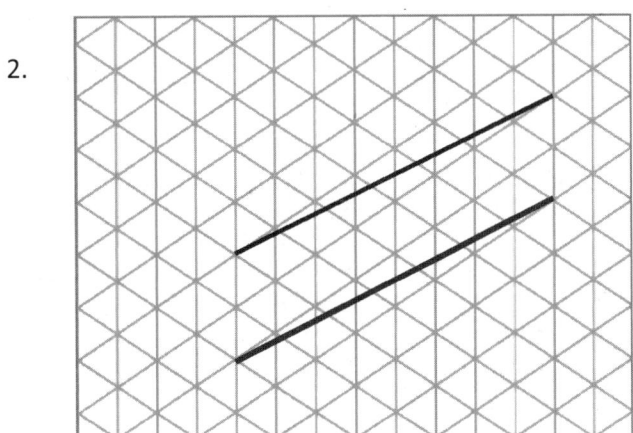

It's tricky to draw diagonal parallel line segments! I draw a line segment that is a distance of two triangle base lengths at every point along the segment.

Lesson 4: Identify, define, and draw parallel lines.

3. Draw a line using your straightedge. Then, use your right angle template and straightedge to construct a line parallel to the first line you drew.

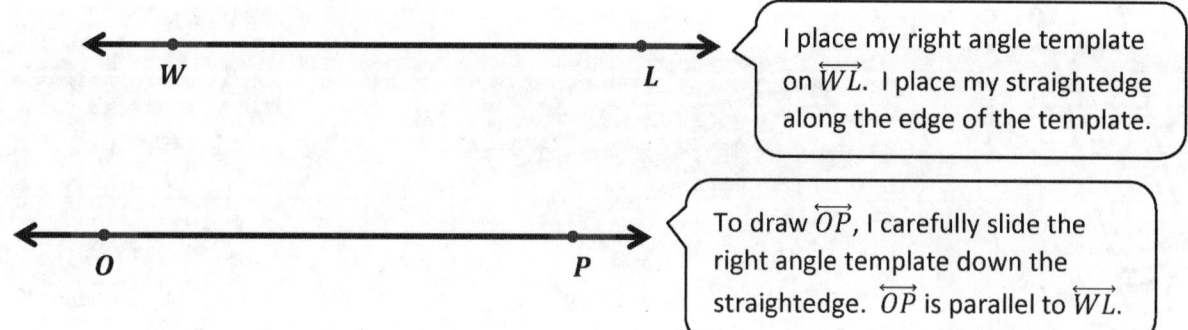

Name _____   Date _____

1. On each object, trace at least one pair of lines that appear to be parallel.

2. How do you know if two lines are parallel?

3. In the square and triangular grids below, use the given segments in each grid to draw a segment that is parallel using a straightedge.

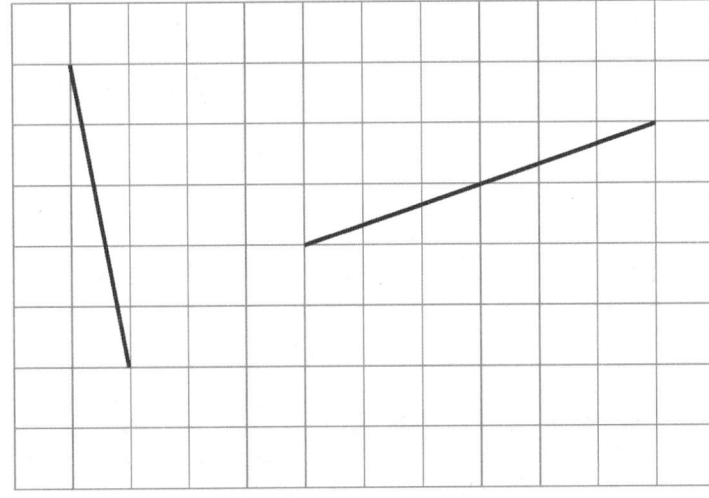 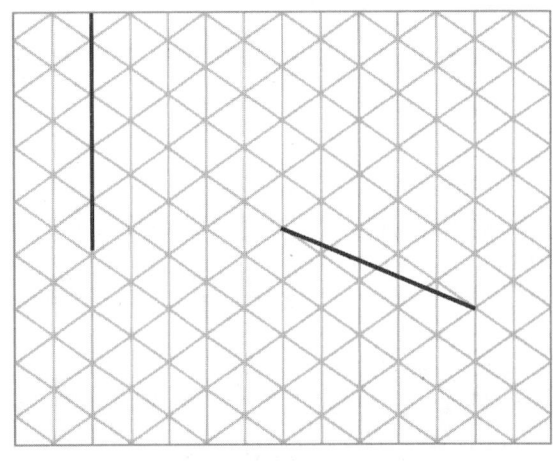

A STORY OF UNITS – TEKS EDITION
Lesson 4 Homework 4•4

4. Determine which of the following figures have sides that are parallel by using a straightedge and the right angle template that you created. Circle the letter of the shapes that have at least one pair of parallel sides. Mark each pair of parallel sides with arrows, and then identify the parallel sides with a statement modeled after the one in 4(a).

(a.) 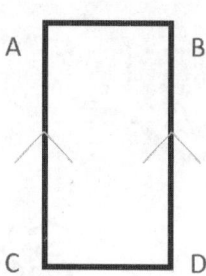 $\overline{AC} \parallel \overline{BD}$

b.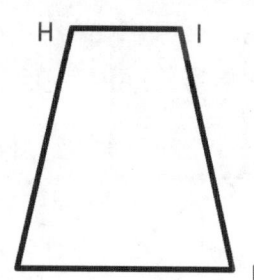

c.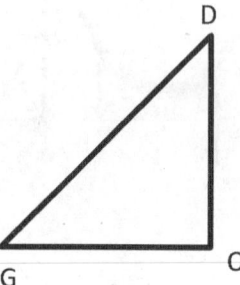

d.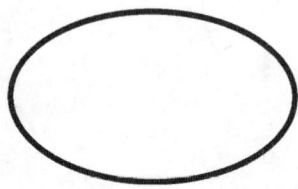

e.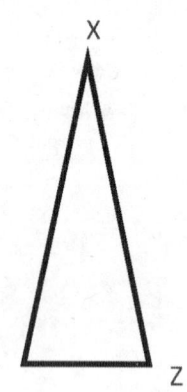

f.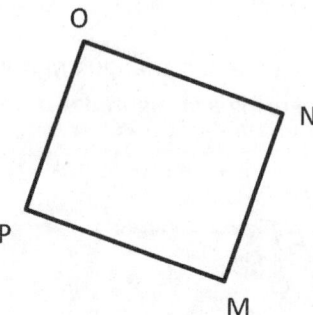

g.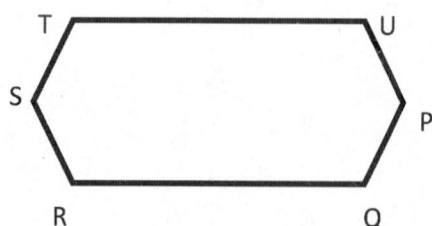

h.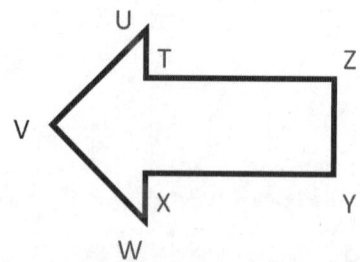

Lesson 4: Identify, define, and draw parallel lines.

5. True or false? All shapes with a right angle have sides that are parallel. Explain your thinking.

6. Explain why $\overline{AB}$ and $\overline{CD}$ are parallel, but $\overline{EF}$ and $\overline{GH}$ are not.

A ——————— B

C ——————— D

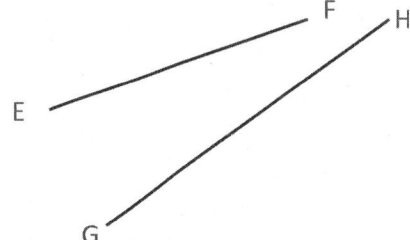

7. Draw a line using your straightedge. Now, use your right angle template and straightedge to construct a line parallel to the first line you drew.

Lesson 4: Identify, define, and draw parallel lines.

A STORY OF UNITS – TEKS EDITION   Lesson 5 Homework Helper 4•4

1. Identify the measures of the following angles.

   The angle measures 80°.

   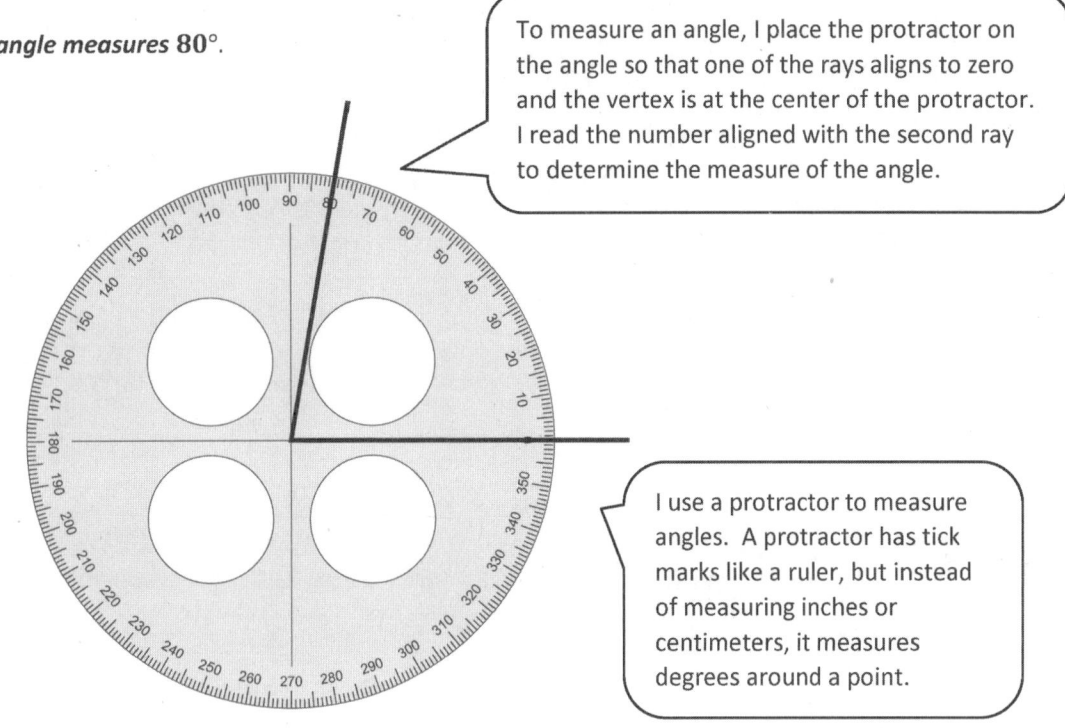

   To measure an angle, I place the protractor on the angle so that one of the rays aligns to zero and the vertex is at the center of the protractor. I read the number aligned with the second ray to determine the measure of the angle.

   I use a protractor to measure angles. A protractor has tick marks like a ruler, but instead of measuring inches or centimeters, it measures degrees around a point.

2. If you didn't have a protractor, how could you construct one? Use words, pictures, or numbers to explain in the space below.

   Sample Student Response:

   If I didn't have a protractor, I could cut out a paper circle. Using a right angle template, I could partition the circle in fourths and then mark 0°, 90°, 180°, 270°, and 360°. Although my protractor would not be able to give an exact measurement of any angle, I could estimate the measure using these benchmarks.

   I reflect on my experiences and discussions in class. We partitioned paper circles in various ways, labeling degrees accurately.

Lesson 5: Use a circular protractor to understand a 1-degree angle as $\frac{1}{360}$ of any circle. Explore benchmark angles using the protractor.

25

Name _____ Date _____

1. Identify the measures of the following angles.

a.
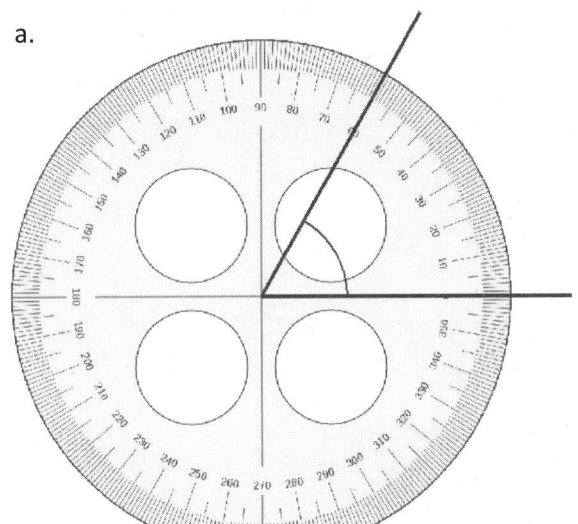

b.
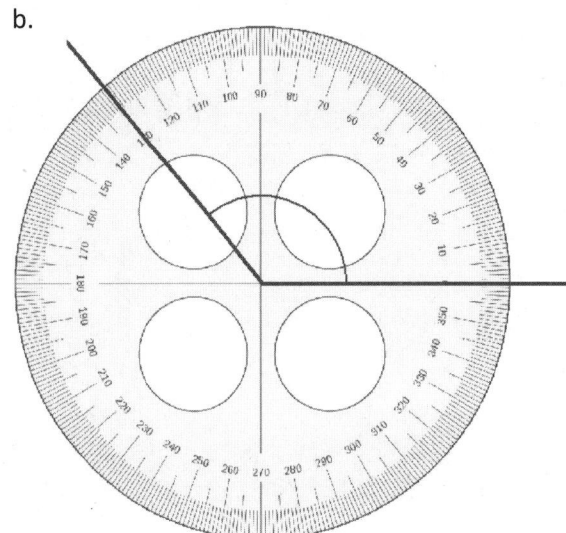

c.
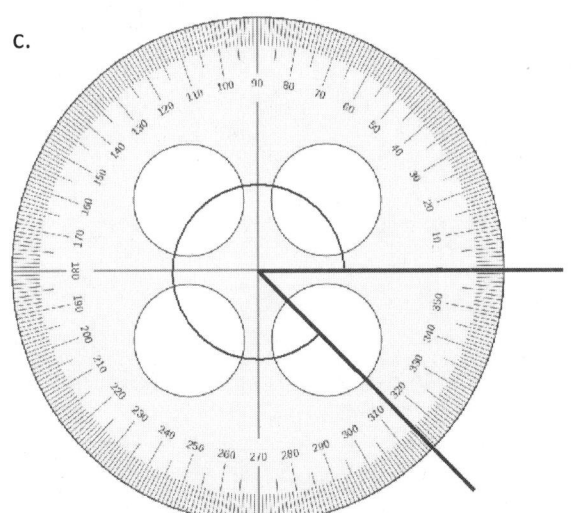

d.
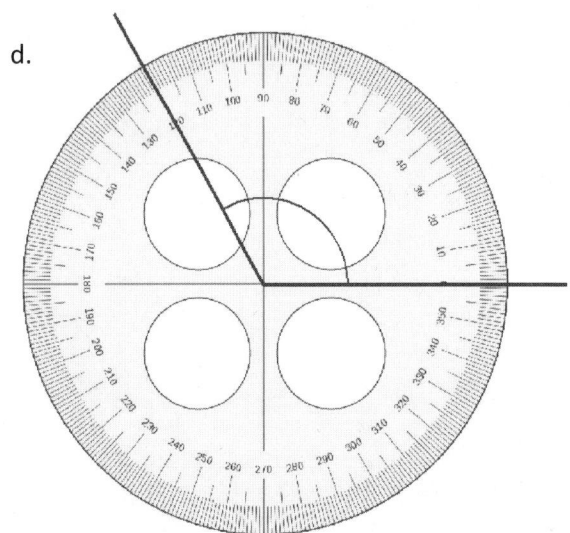

2. If you didn't have a protractor, how could you construct one? Use words, pictures, or numbers to explain in the space below.

1. Use a protractor to measure the angle, and then record the measurement in degrees.

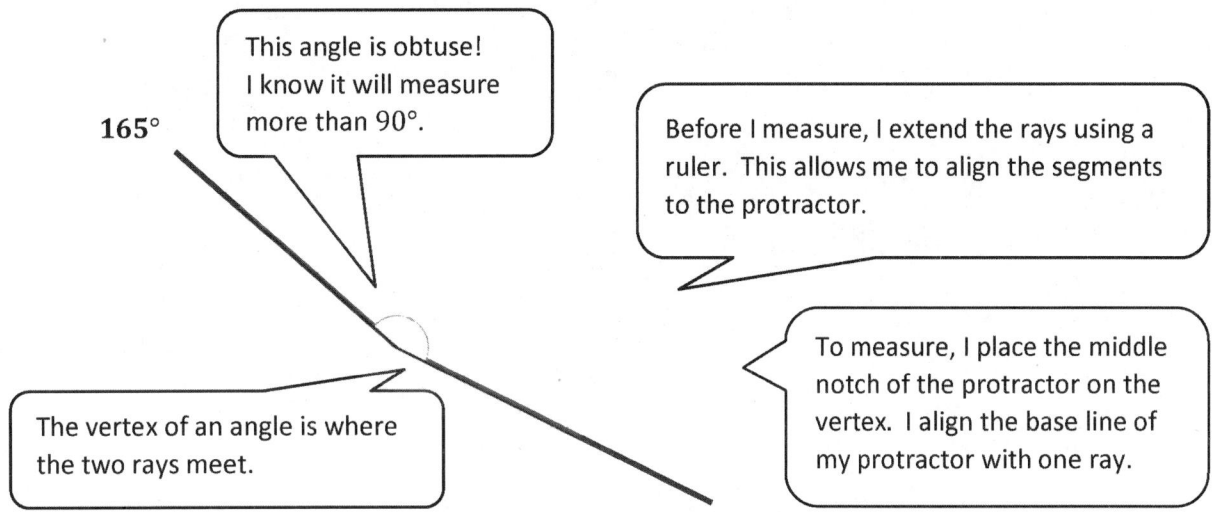

2. Use a protractor to measure the angle. Extend the length of the segments as needed. When you extend the segments, does the angle measure stay the same? Explain how you know.

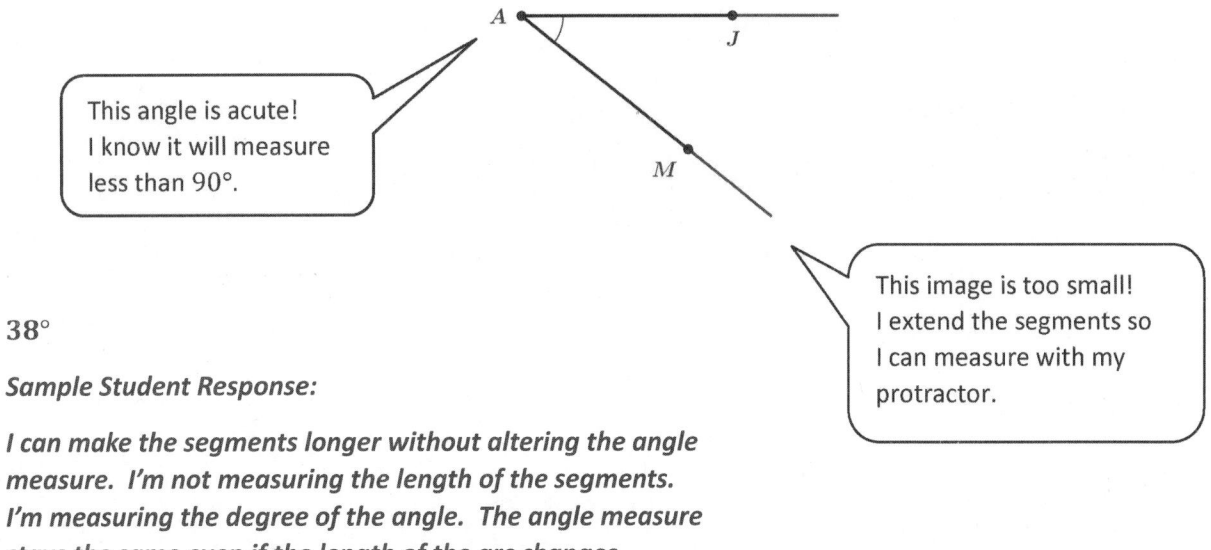

38°

Sample Student Response:

I can make the segments longer without altering the angle measure. I'm not measuring the length of the segments. I'm measuring the degree of the angle. The angle measure stays the same even if the length of the arc changes.

A STORY OF UNITS – TEKS EDITION

Lesson 6 Homework 4•4

Name _____ Date _____

1. Use a protractor to measure the angles, and then record the measurements in degrees.

   a.

   b.

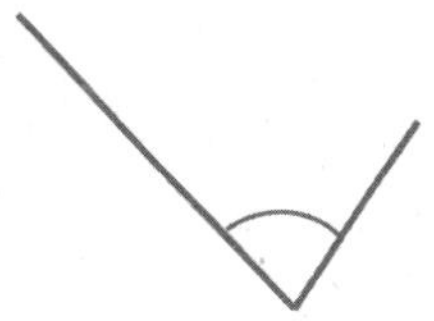

   c.

   d.

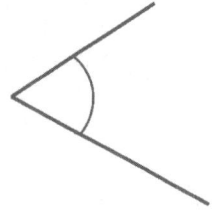

e.

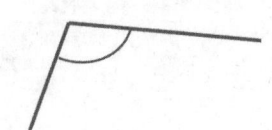

f.

g.

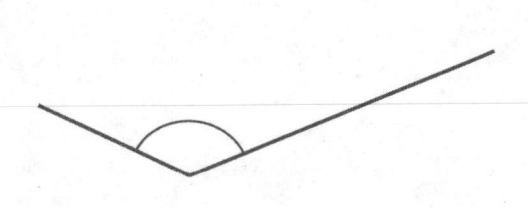

h.

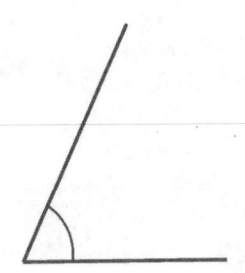

i.

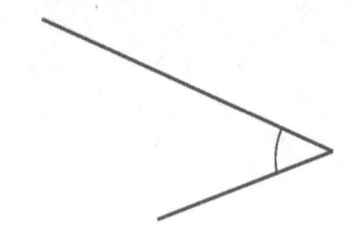

j.

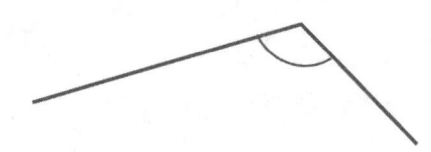

Lesson 6: Use varied protractors to distinguish angle measure from length measurement.

2. Using the green and red circle cutouts from today's lesson, explain to someone at home how the cutouts can be used to show that the angle measures are the same even though the circles are different sizes. Write words to explain what you told him or her.

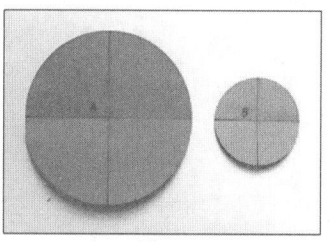

3. Use a protractor to measure each angle. Extend the length of the segments as needed. When you extend the segments, does the angle measure stay the same? Explain how you know.

   a.

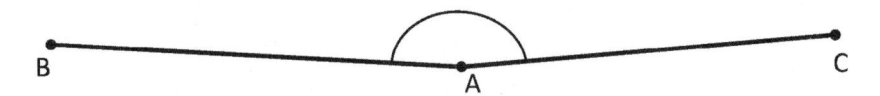

   B — A — C

   b.

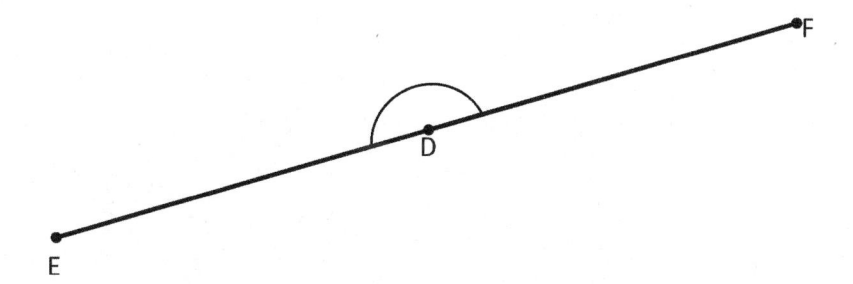

   E — D — F

A STORY OF UNITS – TEKS EDITION

Lesson 7 Homework Helper 4•4

Construct angles that measure the give number of degrees. For the first problem, use the ray shown as one of the rays of the angle with its endpoint as the vertex of the angle. Draw an arc to indicate the angle that was measured.

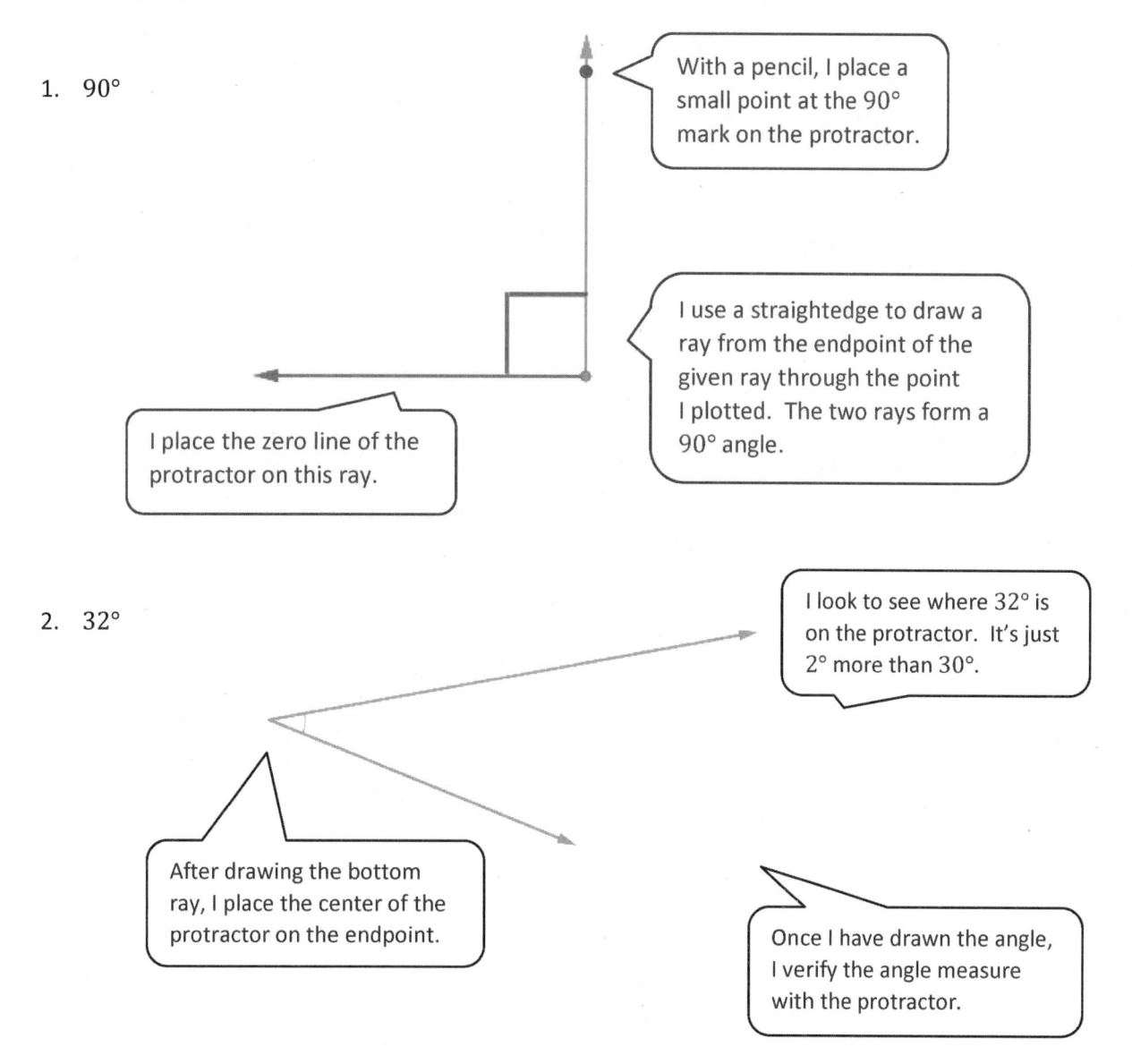

1. 90°

With a pencil, I place a small point at the 90° mark on the protractor.

I use a straightedge to draw a ray from the endpoint of the given ray through the point I plotted. The two rays form a 90° angle.

I place the zero line of the protractor on this ray.

2. 32°

I look to see where 32° is on the protractor. It's just 2° more than 30°.

After drawing the bottom ray, I place the center of the protractor on the endpoint.

Once I have drawn the angle, I verify the angle measure with the protractor.

Lesson 7: Measure and draw angles. Sketch given angle measures, and verify with a protractor.

35

Name _____   Date _____

Construct angles that measure the given number of degrees. For Problems 1–4, use the ray shown as one of the rays of the angle with its endpoint as the vertex of the angle. Draw an arc to indicate the angle that was measured.

1. 25°

2. 85°

3. 140°

4. 83°

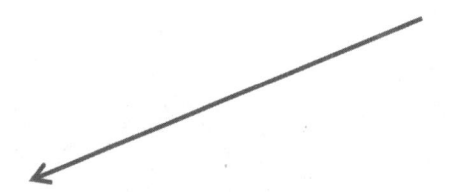

Lesson 7: Measure and draw angles. Sketch given angle measures, and verify with a protractor.

5. 108°

6. 72°

7. 25°

8. 155°

9. 45°

10. 135°

Lesson 7: Measure and draw angles. Sketch given angle measures, and verify with a protractor.

A STORY OF UNITS – TEKS EDITION Lesson 8 Homework Helper 4•4

1. James looked at the clock when he put the cake in the oven and when he took it out. How many degrees did the minute hand turn from start to finish?

start time    end time

The minute hand turned 180°.

I know from Lesson 5 that there are 360° in a full turn. From the 12 to the 3 is a 90° angle, and from the 3 to the 6 is another 90° angle.

2. Delonte turned the lock on his locker one quarter turn to the right and then 180° to the left. Draw a picture showing the position of the lock after he turned it.

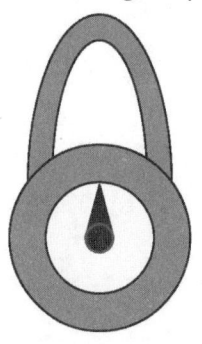

before 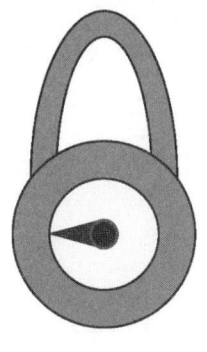   after

I think of the lock as a clock. A quarter-turn to the right is 15 minutes, and 180° to the left is 30 minutes backward.

3. How many quarter-turns does the picture need to be rotated in order for it to be upright?

To be upright, the picture needs to be turned two quarter-turns.

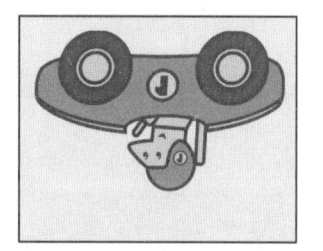

I can turn the paper itself to help me figure out the answer!

Lesson 8: Identify and measure angles as turns and recognize them in various contexts.

A STORY OF UNITS – TEKS EDITION   Lesson 8 Homework   4•4

Name _____   Date _____

1. Jill, Shyan, and Barb stood in the middle of the yard and faced the barn. Jill turned 90° to the right. Shyan turned 180° to the left. Barb turned 270° to the left. Name the object that each girl is now facing.

   Jill _____

   Shyan _____

   Barb _____

2. Allison looked at the clock at the beginning of class and at the end of class. How many degrees did the minute hand turn from the beginning of class until the end?

   Beginning   End

3. The snowboarder went off a jump and did a 180. In which direction was the snowboarder facing when he landed? How do you know?

4. As she drove down the icy road, Mrs. Campbell slammed on her brakes. Her car did a 360. Explain what happened to Mrs. Campbell's car.

Lesson 8: Identify and measure angles as turns and recognize them in various contexts.

5. Jonah turned the knob of the stove two quarter-turns. Draw a picture showing the position of the knob after he turned it.

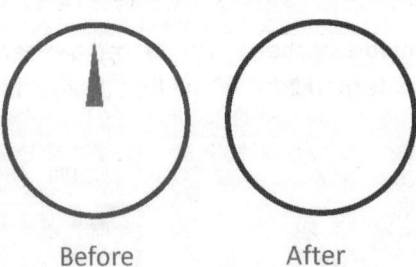

Before   After

6. Betsy used her scissors to cut out a coupon from the newspaper. How many total quarter-turns will she need to rotate the paper in order to cut out the entire coupon?

7. How many quarter-turns does the picture need to be rotated in order for it to be upright?

8. David faced north. He turned 180° to the right, and then 270° to the left. In which direction is he now facing?

A STORY OF UNITS – TEKS EDITION

Lesson 9 Homework Helper 4•4

Pattern Blocks

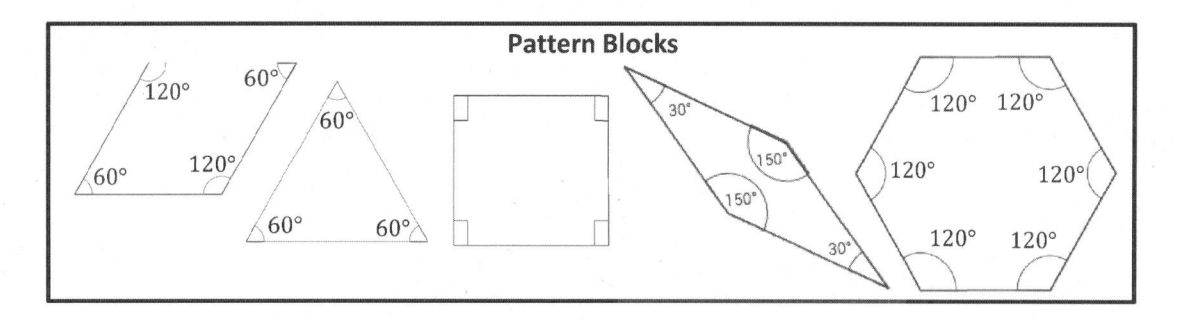

Sketch one way to compose ∠ABC using two or more pattern blocks. Write an addition sentence to show how you composed the given angle.

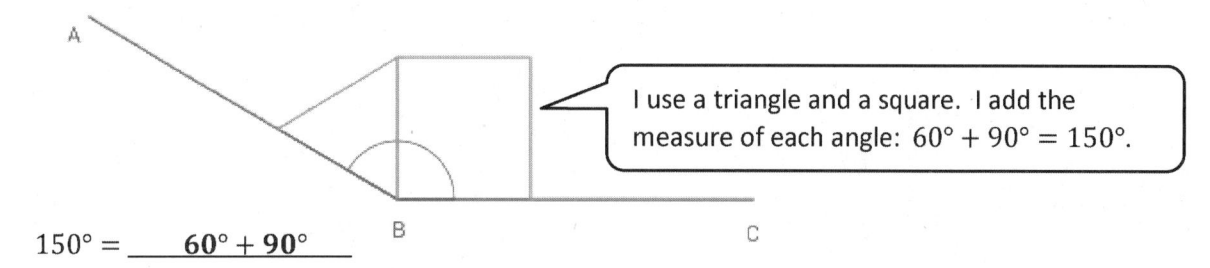

1. ∠ABC = 150°

   150° = __60° + 90°__

   > I use a triangle and a square. I add the measure of each angle: 60° + 90° = 150°.

Sabrina built the following shape with her pattern blocks. As indicated by their arcs, solve for x°, y°, and z°. Write an addition sentence for each. The first one is done for you.

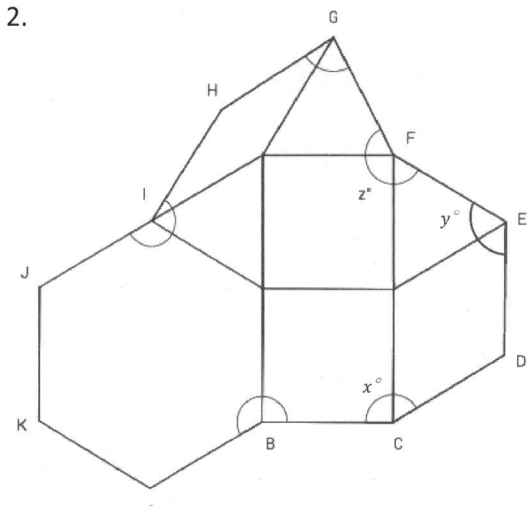

2.
   a. y° = 60° + 60°
      y° = 120°

   b. z° = __60° + 90° + 60°__
      z° = __210°__

   c. x° = __90° + 60°__
      x° = __150°__

   > To determine x°, y°, and z°, I add together the smaller angles encompassed by the arcs. I use the chart at the top of the page to determine the measure of each of the smaller angles.

Lesson 9: Decompose angles using pattern blocks.

A STORY OF UNITS – TEKS EDITION

Lesson 9 Homework 4•4

Name _____   Date _____

Sketch two different ways to compose the given angles using two or more pattern blocks. Write an addition sentence to show how you composed the given angle.

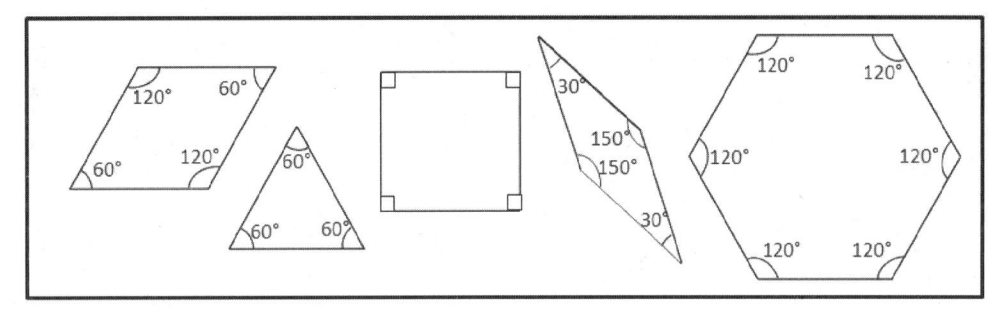

1. Points A, B, and C form a straight line.

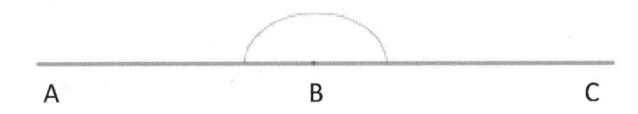

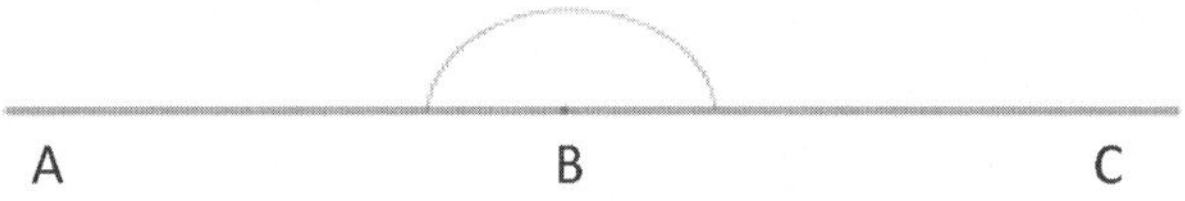

A ——————— B ——————— C   A ——————— B ——————— C

180° = _____   180° = _____

2. ∠DEF = 90°

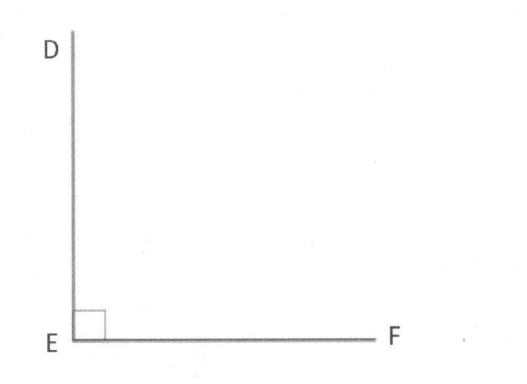

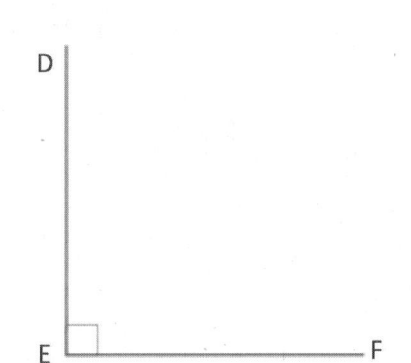

D   D
| |
| |
|_____ F |_____ F
E   E

90° = _____   90° = _____

Lesson 9: Decompose angles using pattern blocks.

45

3. ∠GHI = 120°

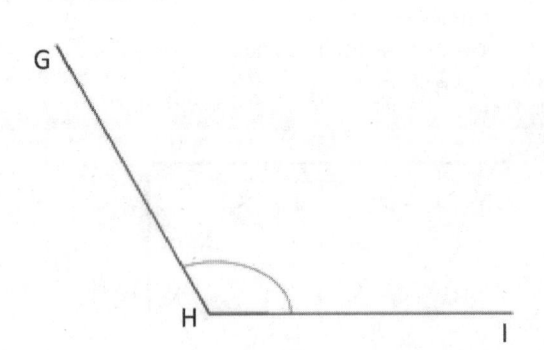

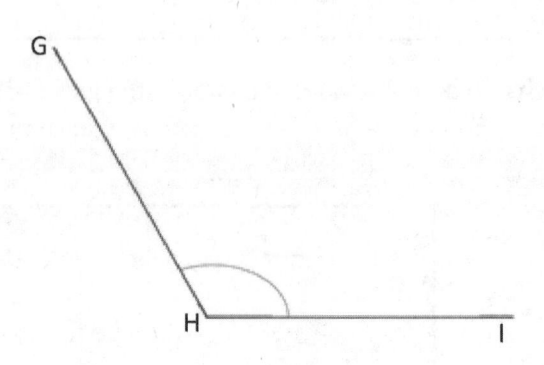

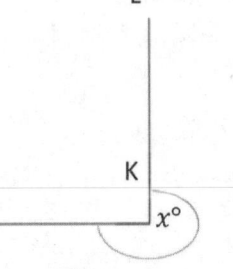

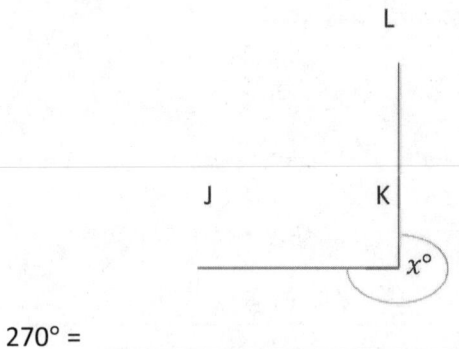

120° = _____

120° = _____

4. $x° = 270°$

270° = _____

270° = _____

5. Micah built the following shape with his pattern blocks. Write an addition sentence for each angle indicated by an arc and solve. The first one is done for you.

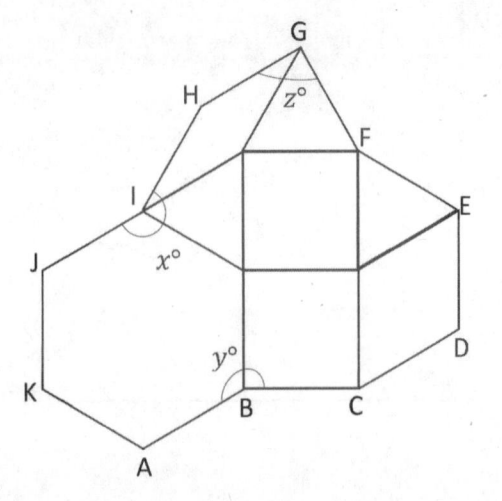

a. $y° = 120° + 90°$

$y° = 210°$

b. $z° =$ _____

$z° =$ _____

c. $x° =$ _____

$x° =$ _____

Lesson 9: Decompose angles using pattern blocks.

A STORY OF UNITS – TEKS EDITION   Lesson 10 Homework Helper   4•4

1. Write an equation, and solve for the measurement of ∠x. Verify the measurement using a protractor.

   a. ∠JKL is a straight angle.

   b. Solve for the measurement of ∠USW. ∠RST is a straight angle.

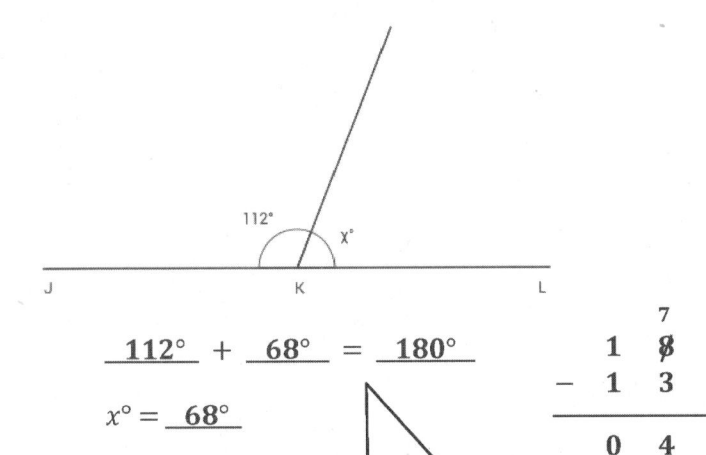

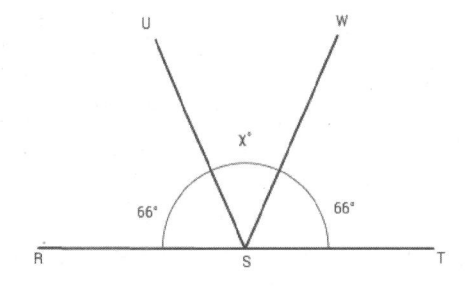

   $112° + 68° = 180°$

   $x° = 68°$

   $$\begin{array}{r} 710 \\ 1\cancel{8}\cancel{0} \\ -132 \\ \hline 048 \end{array}$$

   $66° + 66° + x° = 180°$
   $132° + x° = 180°$
   $x° = 48°$
   ∠USW = 48°

   I know a straight angle measures 180°. I subtract 112° from 180° to find the value of $x°$. To verify my answer, I use my protractor to measure the angle. It measures 68°.

   I know that the sum of these three angle measures is 180°. I add the two parts that I know and then I subtract their total from 180°.

2. Complete the following directions in the space to the right.

   a. Draw 2 points: S and T. Using a straightedge, draw $\overleftrightarrow{ST}$.
   b. Plot a point U somewhere between points S and T.
   c. Plot a point W, which is not on $\overleftrightarrow{ST}$.
   d. Draw $\overline{UW}$.
   e. Find the measure of ∠SUW and ∠TUW.
   f. Write an equation to show that the angles add to the measure of a straight angle.

   Sample Response:

   I draw the figure. I use my protractor to measure ∠SUW and ∠TUW.

   ∠SUW = 152°
   ∠TUW = 28°
   152° + 28° = 180°

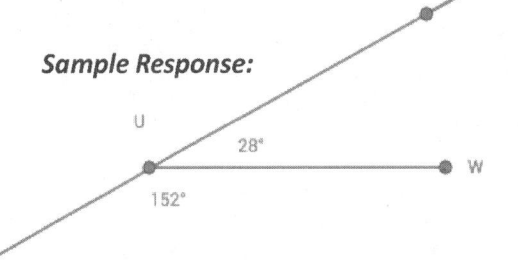

   Lesson 10: Use the addition of adjacent angle measures to solve problems using a letter for the unknown angle measure.

   47

Name _____   Date _____

Write an equation, and solve for the measurement of ∠x. Verify the measurement using a protractor.

1. ∠DCB is a right angle.

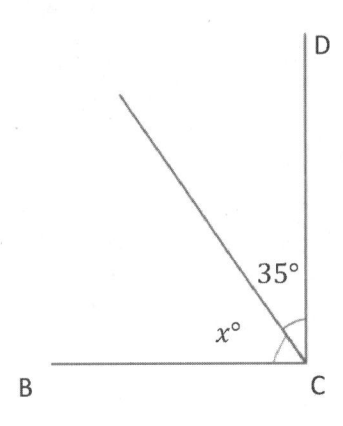

_____ + 35° = 90°

$x° =$ _____

2. ∠HGF is a right angle.

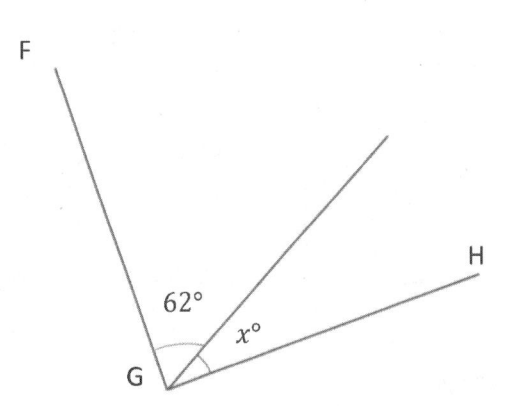

_____ + _____ = _____

$x° =$ _____

3. ∠JKL is a straight angle.

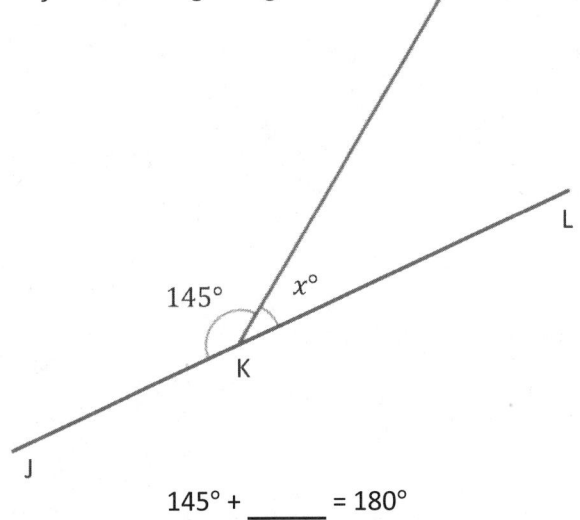

145° + _____ = 180°

$x° =$ _____

4. ∠PQR is a straight angle.

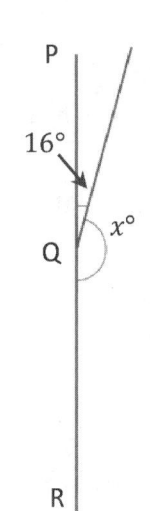

_____ + _____ = _____

$x° =$ _____

Write an equation, and solve for the unknown angle measurements.

5. Solve for the measurement of ∠USW.
   ∠RST is a straight angle.

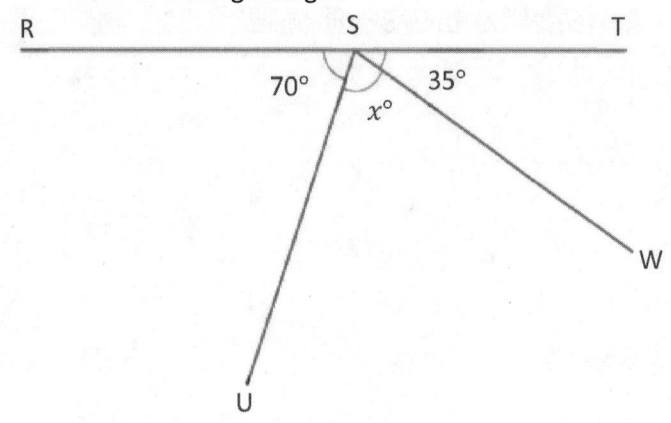

6. Solve for the measurement of ∠OML.
   ∠LMN is a straight angle.

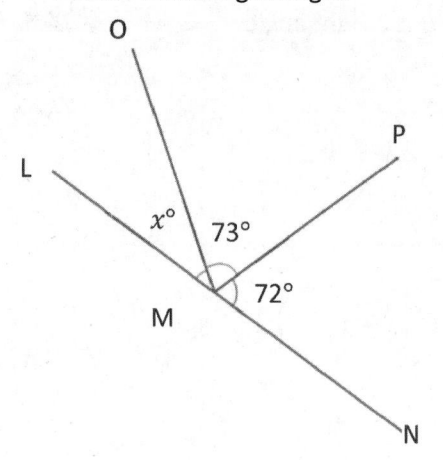

7. In the following figure, DEFH is a rectangle. Without using a protractor, determine the measurement of ∠GEF. Write an equation that could be used to solve the problem.

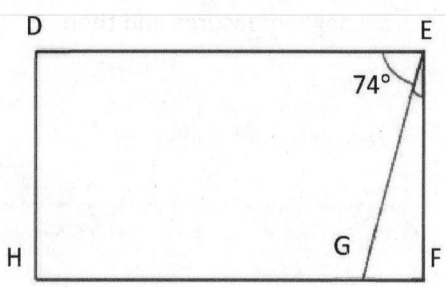

8. Complete the following directions in the space to the right.

   a. Draw 2 points: Q and R. Using a straightedge, draw $\overleftrightarrow{QR}$.
   b. Plot a point S somewhere between points Q and R.
   c. Plot a point T, which is not on $\overleftrightarrow{QR}$.
   d. Draw $\overline{TS}$.
   e. Find the measure of ∠QST and ∠RST.
   f. Write an equation to show that the angles add to the measure of a straight angle.

A STORY OF UNITS – TEKS EDITION

Lesson 11 Homework Helper   4•4

Write an equation, and solve for the unknown angle measurements numerically.

1.

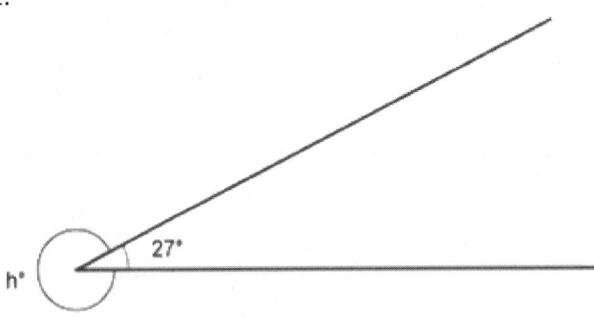

> I know from Lesson 5 that a circle measures 360°. I solve for $h°$ by subtracting 27° from 360°.

$27°$ + $333°$ = 360°

$h° =$ $333°$

```
     5 10
  3  6̸  0̸
-    2  7
---------
  3  3  3
```

2.

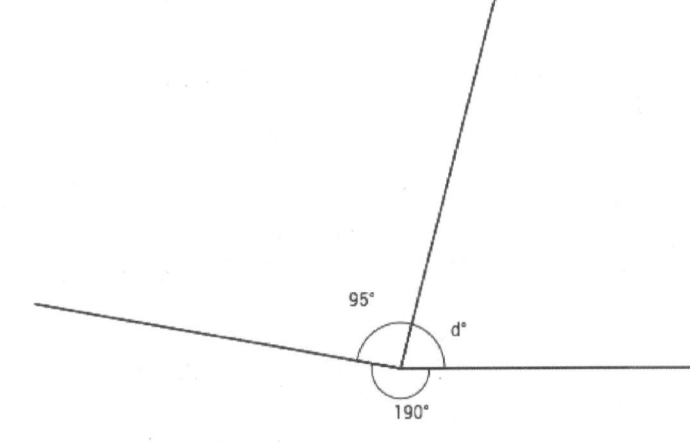

> I solve for $d°$ by adding together the known angle measures and then subtracting their sum from 360°.

$190°$ + $95°$ + $75°$ = $360°$

$d° =$ $75°$

```
    1 9 0
+     9 5
    ¹
---------
    2 8 5
```

```
        15
     2  5̸ 10
     3̸  6̸  0̸
-    2  8  5
------------
        7  5
```

Lesson 11:   Use the addition of adjacent angle measures to solve problems using a letter for the unknown angle measure.

A STORY OF UNITS – TEKS EDITION   Lesson 11 Homework Helper   4•4

3. T is the intersection of $\overline{UV}$ and $\overline{WX}$. $g° = \underline{\ 129°\ }$ $h° = \underline{\ 51°\ }$ $i° = \underline{\ 129°\ }$
   $\angle UTW$ is 51°.

$$129° + h° = 180° \qquad 51° + i° = 180°$$
$$h° = 51° \qquad\qquad i° = 129°$$

I can solve for $i°$ by thinking of its relationship to either $\overline{UV}$ or $\overline{WX}$. But I also notice that opposite angles measure the same for this figure.

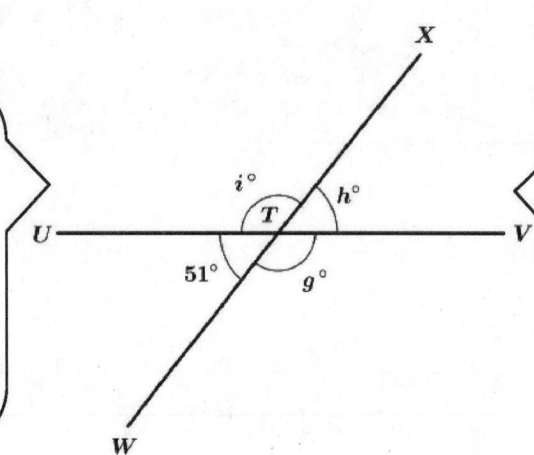

I solve for $h°$ by thinking about the relationships of $\angle WTV$ and $\angle VTX$. Both angle measures add to 180° because they are on $\overline{WX}$.

$$51° + g° = 180°$$
$$g° = 129°$$

I solve for $g°$ by thinking of its relationship to $\angle UTW$. $\angle UTV$ is a straight angle that measures 180°.

```
       7 10
   1   8̸  0̸
 −     5  1
 ─────────────
   1   2  9
```

Lesson 11: Use the addition of adjacent angle measures to solve problems using a letter for the unknown angle measure.

A STORY OF UNITS – TEKS EDITION   Lesson 11 Homework Helper   4•4

4. P is the intersection of $\overline{QR}$, $\overline{ST}$, and $\overline{UP}$. $j° =$ __124°__ $k° =$ __56°__ $m° =$ __34°__
   ∠QPS is 56°.

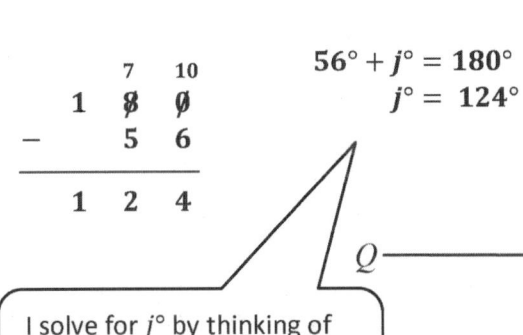

$$56° + j° = 180°$$
$$j° = 124°$$

$$\begin{array}{r} 710 \\ 1\cancel{8}\cancel{0} \\ -56 \\ \hline 124 \end{array}$$

I solve for $j°$ by thinking of the relationship ∠SPQ and ∠QPT have to $\overline{ST}$.

$$124° + k° = 180°$$
$$k° = 56°$$

$$\begin{array}{r} 710 \\ 1\cancel{8}\cancel{0} \\ -124 \\ \hline 056 \end{array}$$

I solve for $k°$ by thinking of the relationship ∠QPT and ∠TPR have to $\overline{QR}$.

I solve for $m°$ by noticing that ∠UPR is a right angle; therefore, ∠UPQ is also a right angle.

$$56° + m° = 90°$$
$$m° = 34°$$

$$\begin{array}{r} 810 \\ \cancel{9}\cancel{0} \\ -56 \\ \hline 34 \end{array}$$

Lesson 11: Use the addition of adjacent angle measures to solve problems using a letter for the unknown angle measure.

53

Name _____ **Date** _____

Write an equation, and solve for the unknown angle measurements numerically.

1.

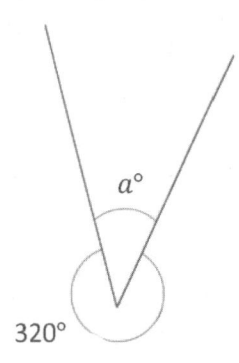

   $a°$

   320°

   _____° + 320° = 360°

   $a° =$ _____°

2.

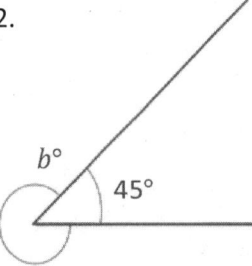

   $b°$ 45°

   _____° + _____° = 360°

   $b° =$ _____°

3.

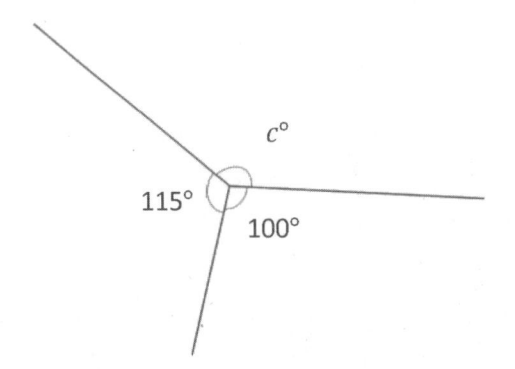

   $c°$
   115°   100°

   _____° + _____° + _____° = _____°

   $c° =$ _____°

4.

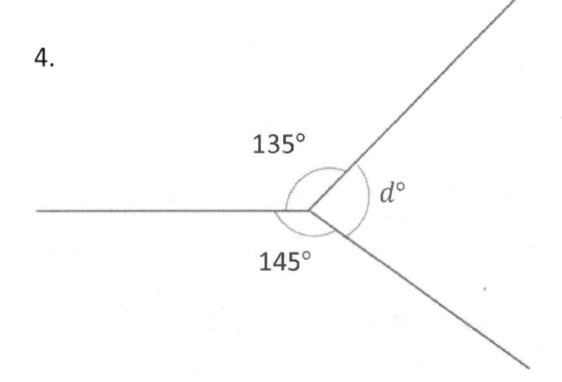

   135° $d°$
   145°

   _____° + _____° + _____° = _____°

   $d° =$ _____°

A STORY OF UNITS – TEKS EDITION Lesson 11 Homework 4•4

Write an equation, and solve for the unknown angles numerically.

5. O is the intersection of $\overline{AB}$ and $\overline{CD}$. $e° =$ _____ $f° =$ _____
   $\angle COB$ is 145°, and $\angle AOC$ is 35°.

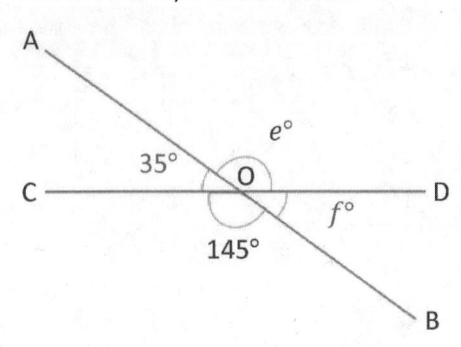

6. O is the intersection of $\overline{QR}$ and $\overline{ST}$. $g° =$ _____ $h° =$ _____ $i° =$ _____
   $\angle QOS$ is 55°.

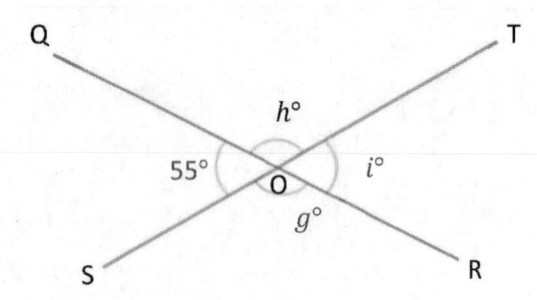

7. O is the intersection of $\overline{UP}$, $\overline{WX}$, and $\overline{YO}$. $j° =$ _____ $k° =$ _____ $m° =$ _____
   $\angle VOX$ is 46°.

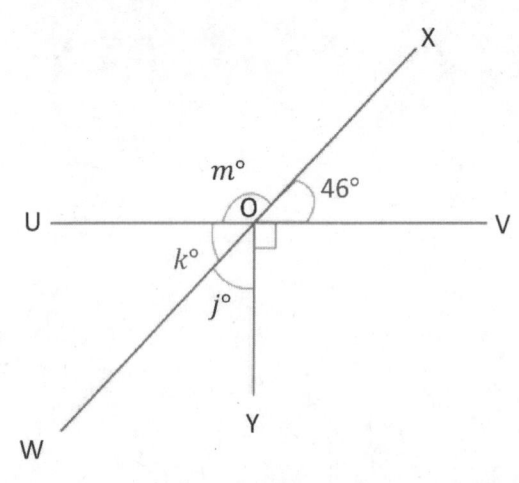

A STORY OF UNITS – TEKS EDITION Lesson 12 Homework Helper 4•4

> I can tell parts (b) and (d) each have a line of symmetry because the figure in each part is the same on both sides of the line.

1. Circle the figures that have a correct line of symmetry drawn.

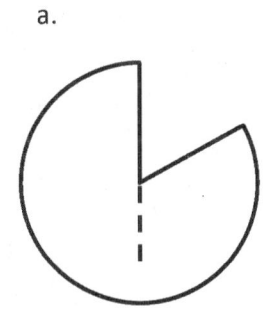

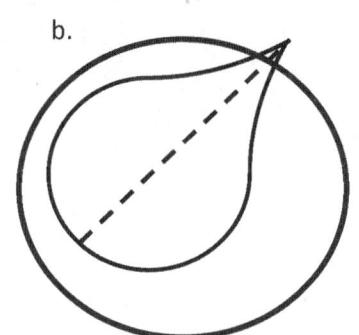

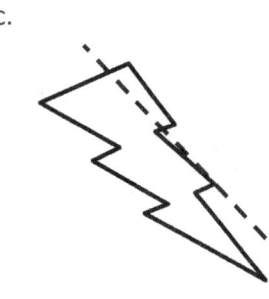

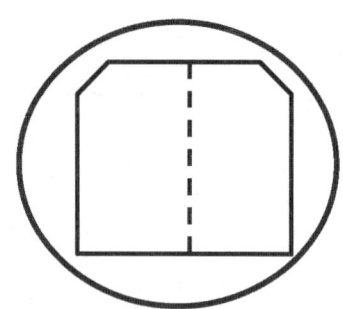

   a.   b.   c.   d.

2. Find and draw all lines of symmetry for the following figures. Write the number of lines of symmetry that you found in the blank underneath the shape.

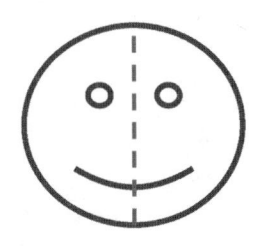

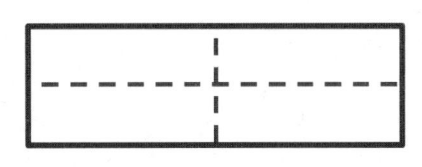

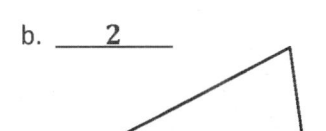

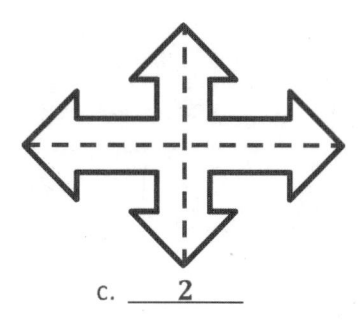

   a. __1__   b. __2__   c. __2__

> I think about folding these shapes in half many different ways. If the shapes match where I fold them, that is a line of symmetry.

Lesson 12: Recognize lines of symmetry for given two-dimensional figures. Identify line-symmetric figures, and draw lines of symmetry.

3. Half of the figure below has been drawn. Use the line of symmetry, represented by the dashed line, to complete the figure.

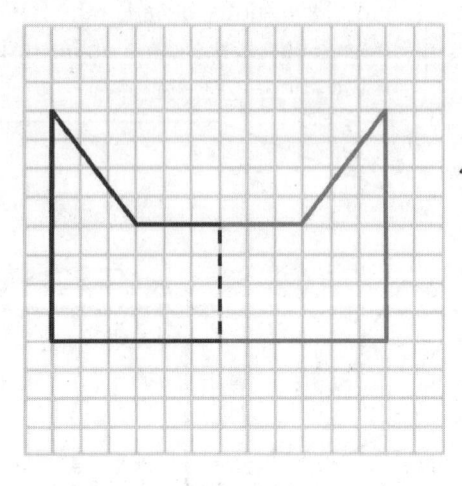

I use the grid to help me complete the figure. I count how many units long each segment is, and then I draw segments of the same length for the other half of the figure. I draw the sides that follow the grid lines first, and then I make the diagonal line.

A STORY OF UNITS – TEKS EDITION   Lesson 12 Homework 4•4

Name _____   Date _____

1. Circle the figures that have a correct line of symmetry drawn.

   a. 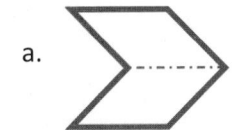   b. 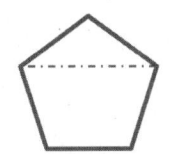   c.    d.

2. Find and draw all lines of symmetry for the following figures. Write the number of lines of symmetry that you found in the blank underneath the shape.

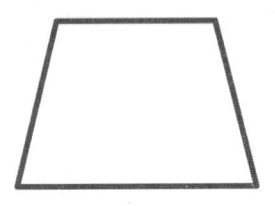

   a. _____   b. 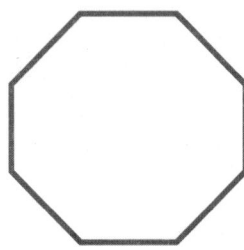 _____   c. _____

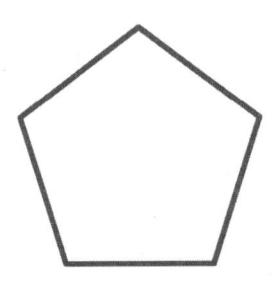

   d. 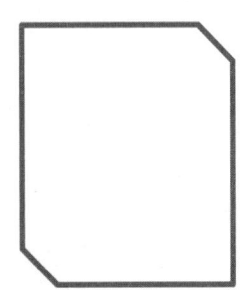 _____   e.  _____   f. _____

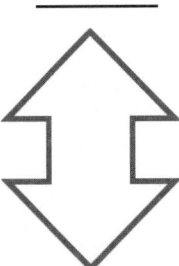

   g. 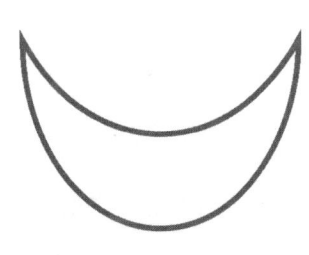 _____   h. 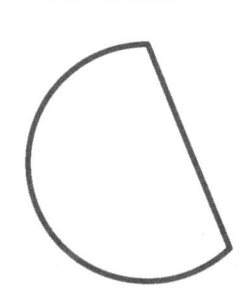 _____   i. _____

3. Half of each figure below has been drawn. Use the line of symmetry, represented by the dashed line, to complete each figure.

   a.

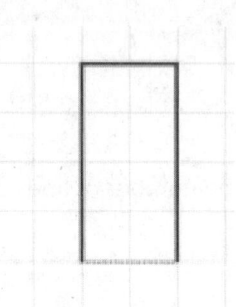

   b.

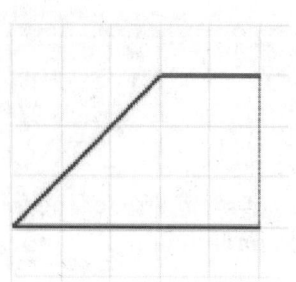

   c.

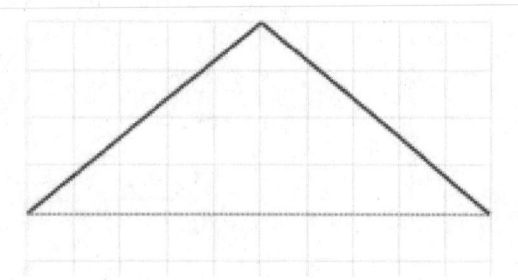

   d.

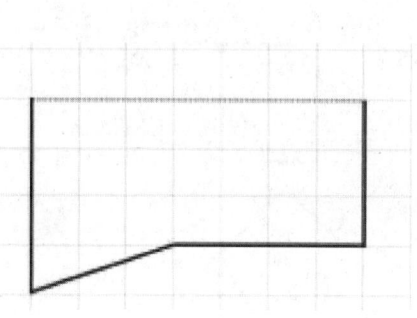

4. Is there another shape that has the same number of lines of symmetry as a circle? Explain.

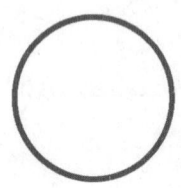

A STORY OF UNITS – TEKS EDITION Lesson 13 Homework Helper 4•4

1. Classify each triangle by its angle measurements. Circle the correct names.

	Classify Using Angle Measurements
a.	Acute **(Right)** Obtuse
b.	Acute Right **(Obtuse)**
c.	**(Acute)** Right Obtuse

> Sometimes triangles are drawn with tick marks, little dashes perpendicular to the sides of the triangle. These tick marks mean that those sides have the same length.

> To classify by angle measure, I can use a protractor or a right angle template. An acute triangle has three angles less than 90°.
> A right triangle has one 90° angle. An obtuse triangle has one angle greater than 90°.

Lesson 13: Analyze and classify triangles based on angle measure.

A STORY OF UNITS – TEKS EDITION   Lesson 13 Homework Helper   4•4

2. Use a ruler to connect points to form two other triangles. Use each point only once. None of the triangles may overlap. One point will be unused. Name and classify the three triangles below. The first one has been done for you.

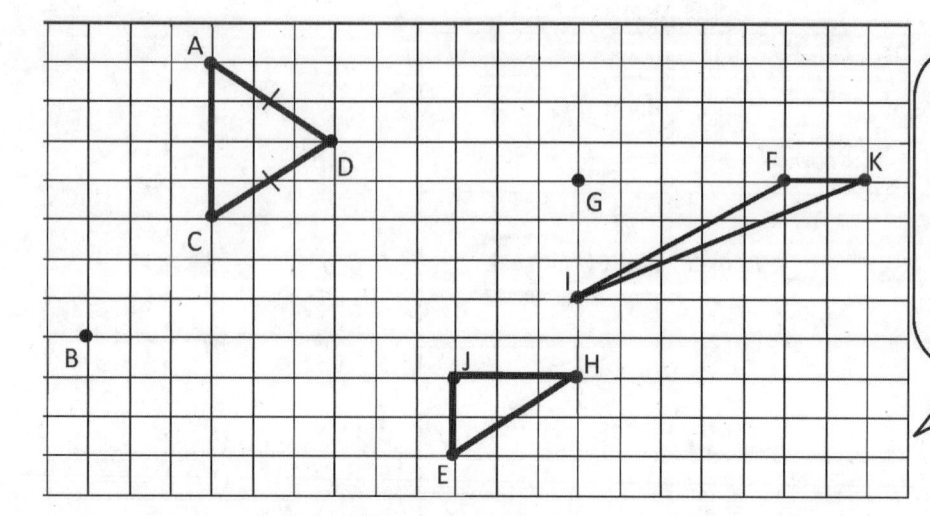

> I draw two triangles and then classify each of them. I look back to the first problem to recall how to classify the triangles.

Name the Triangles Using Vertices	Classify by Angle Measurement
△ FKI	Obtuse
△ ACD	Acute
△ EHJ	Right

3. Can a triangle have two obtuse angles? Explain.

   Sample answer:

   No, if a triangle had two obtuse angles, the three sides could never meet.

   > I draw two obtuse angles, and I see that the three sides can't form a triangle since two of the line segments will continue to get farther apart instead of closer together if I make them longer.

Lesson 13: Analyze and classify triangles based on angle measure.

Name _____   Date _____

1. Classify each triangle by its angle measurements. Circle the correct names.

	Classify Using Angle Measurements
a. 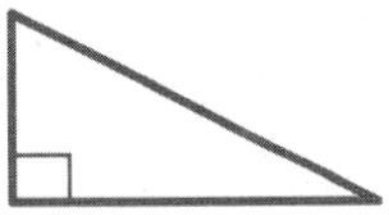	Acute Right Obtuse
b. 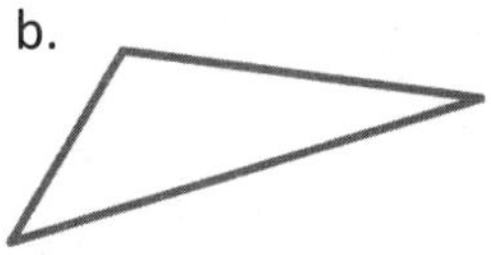	Acute Right Obtuse
c. 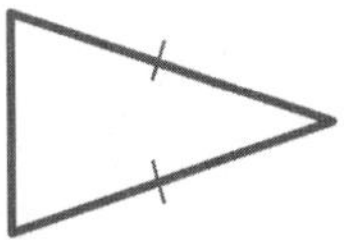	Acute Right Obtuse
d. 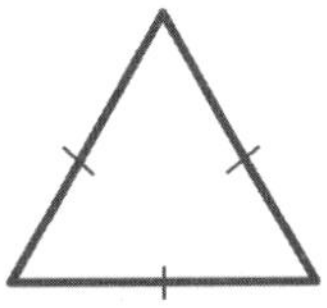	Acute Right Obtuse

2. Use a ruler to connect points to form two triangles for each classification. Use each point only once. None of the triangles may overlap. The first one has been done for you.

   a. Draw and name two right triangles.

   ΔDCH

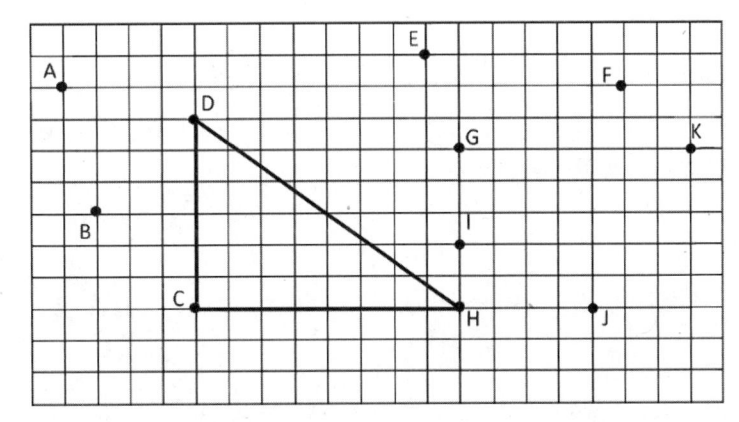

b. Draw and name two obtuse triangles.

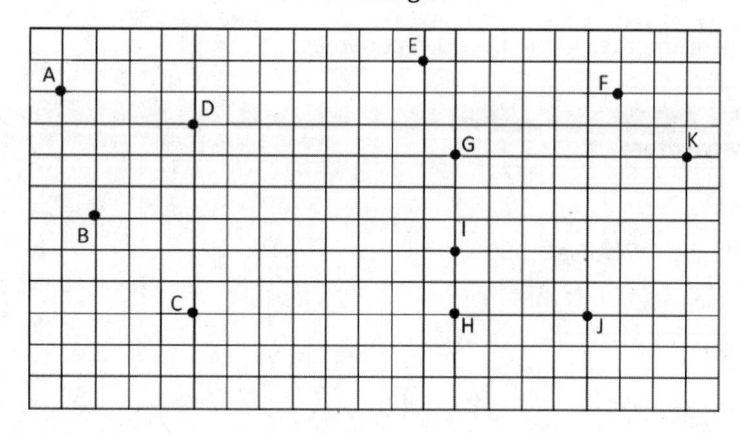

c. Draw and name two acute triangles.

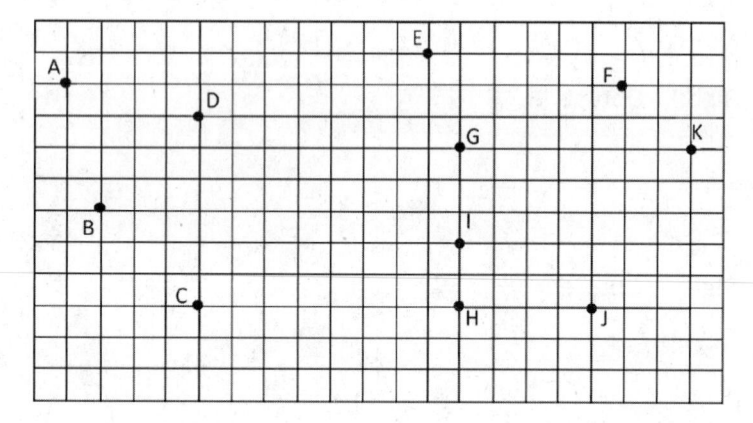

3. Can a triangle have more than one obtuse angle? Explain.

4. Can a triangle have one obtuse angle and one right angle? Explain.

A STORY OF UNITS – TEKS EDITION

Lesson 14 Homework Helper 4•4

1. Draw triangles that fit the following classifications. Use a ruler and protractor. Label the angles.

   a. Acute

   b. Right

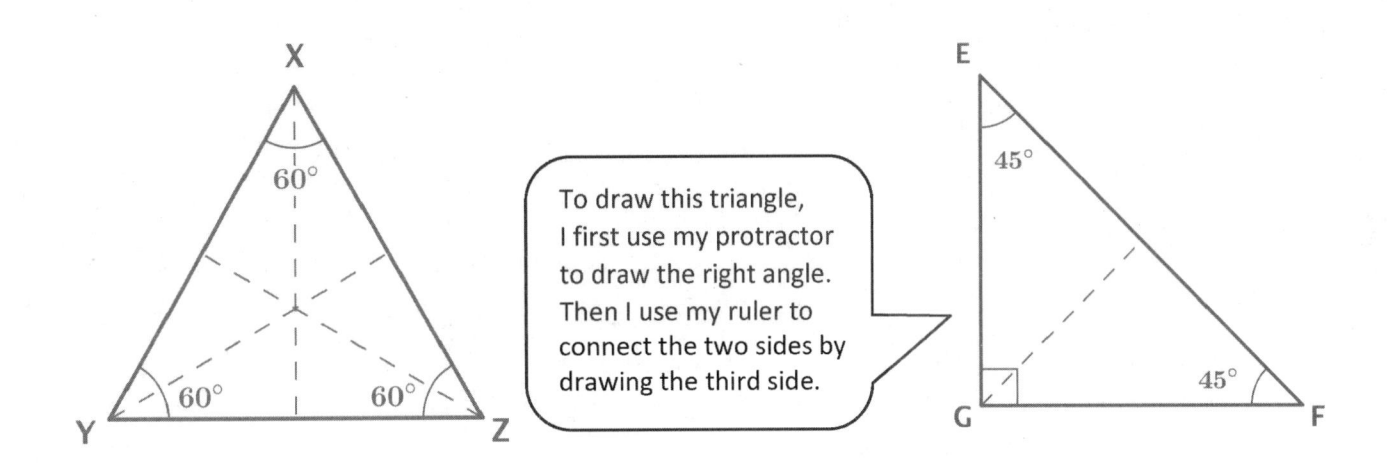

Triangle XYZ with all angles labeled 60°, with three dashed lines of symmetry from each vertex to the midpoint of the opposite side.

To draw this triangle, I first use my protractor to draw the right angle. Then I use my ruler to connect the two sides by drawing the third side.

Triangle EFG with right angle at G, 45° at E and 45° at F, with a dashed line of symmetry from G to the midpoint of EF.

2. Draw all possible lines of symmetry in the triangles above.

   △ XYZ has three lines of symmetry.
   △ EFG has one line of symmetry.

3. △ EFG can be described as a right triangle. True or False?

   Sample answer:

   True. △ EFG **is right. I know this because there is a right angle.**

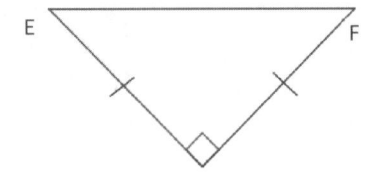

Triangle with vertices E (upper left), F (upper right), and a bottom vertex showing a right angle, with tick marks on both upper sides indicating equal lengths.

Lesson 14: Define and construct triangles from given criteria.

Name _____   Date _____

1. Draw triangles that fit the following classifications. Use a ruler and protractor. Label the angles.

   a. Right triangle with the right angle opening to the top of the page

   b. Right triangle with the right angle opening to the bottom of the page

   c. Obtuse triangle with the obtuse angle opening to the left

   d. Acute triangle

2. Draw all possible lines of symmetry in the triangles above. Explain why some of the triangles do not have lines of symmetry.

Lesson 14: Define and construct triangles from given criteria.

Are the following statements true or false? Explain.

3. A triangle cannot have both an acute angle and a right angle. True or false?

4. △ XYZ can be described as an acute triangle. True or false?

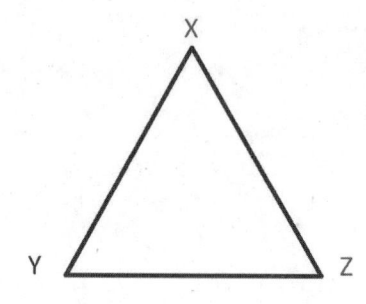

5. A triangle can have more than one right angle. True or false?

A STORY OF UNITS – TEKS EDITION   Lesson 15 Homework Helper   4•4

> I use what I learned in Lessons 3 and 4 to draw parallel and perpendicular lines using a right angle template and a ruler.

Construct the following figures based on the given attributes. Give a name to each figure you construct. Be as specific as possible.

1. A quadrilateral with opposite sides the same length and four right angles

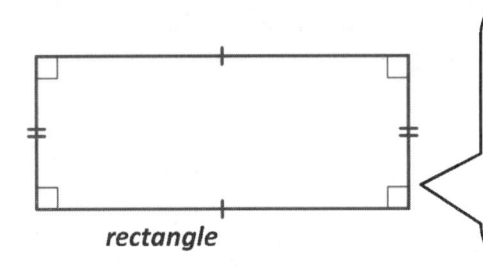

   rectangle

   > I draw the bottom segment using my ruler. I draw the two sides using my right angle template and ruler to make right angles and to make the left and right side lengths equal. I draw the top segment perpendicular to the sides and parallel to the bottom segment. I draw small squares to show the right angles and tick marks to show which sides are equal.

2. A quadrilateral with exactly one set of parallel sides

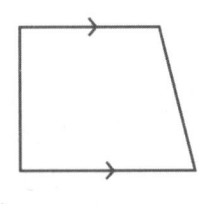

   trapezoid

   > I draw a horizontal segment. I draw a segment that is parallel to the first segment. I connect the endpoints of the segments. I draw arrows to label the parallel sides.

3. A quadrilateral with two sets of parallel sides

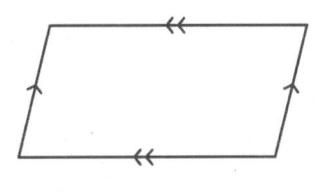

   parallelogram

   > I start by drawing horizontal, parallel sides just as when I started drawing a trapezoid. After I draw the left side segment, I make sure the right side segment is parallel to it. I add arrows on the opposite segments to show they are parallel to each other.

Lesson 15: Classify quadrilaterals based on parallel and perpendicular lines and the presence or absence of angles of a specified size.

4. A parallelogram with all sides the same length and four right angles

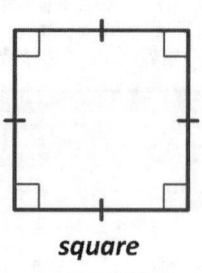

square

> I start by drawing a parallelogram, except I draw the left side segment perpendicular to the horizontal segments. I measure the left side segment and make sure to make the top and bottom segments the same lengths. I draw a right segment perpendicular to the top and bottom segments. It will be the same length as all other sides. I add tick marks and right angle squares.

Name _____   Date _____

1. Use the word bank to name each shape, being as specific as possible.

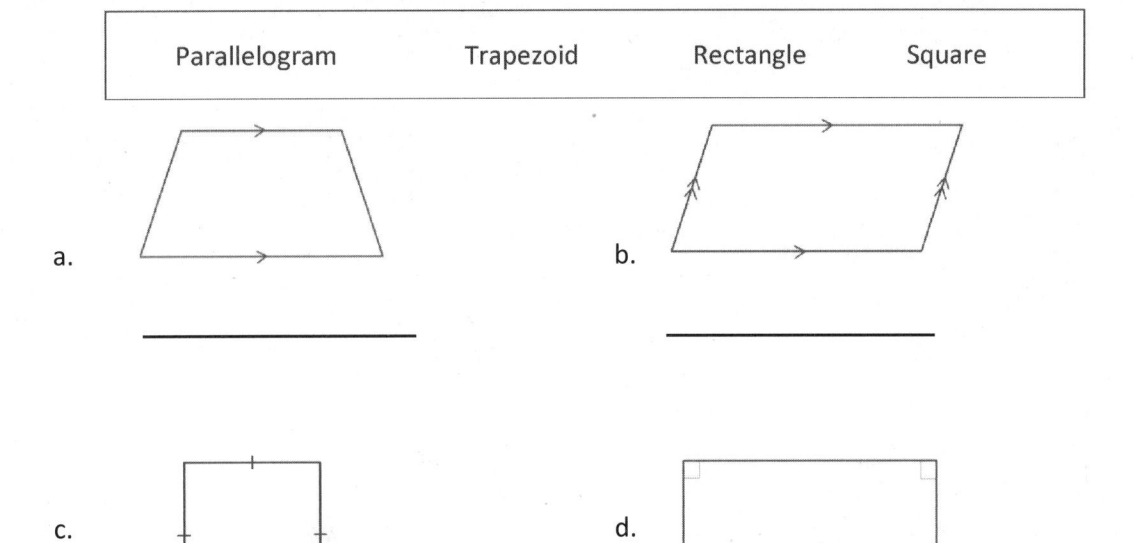

   | Parallelogram | Trapezoid | Rectangle | Square |

   a. _____

   b. _____

   c. _____

   d. _____

2. Explain the attribute that makes a square a special rectangle.

3. Explain the attribute that makes a rectangle a special parallelogram.

4. Explain the attribute that makes a parallelogram a special quadrilateral.

5. Construct the following figures based on the given attributes. Give a name to each figure you construct. Be as specific as possible.

   a. A quadrilateral with four sides the same length and four right angles.

   b. A quadrilateral with two sets of parallel sides.

   c. A quadrilateral with exactly one set of parallel sides.

   d. A parallelogram with four right angles.

A STORY OF UNITS – TEKS EDITION

Lesson 16 Homework Helper 4•4

1. Construct a quadrilateral with all sides of equal length. What shape did you create?

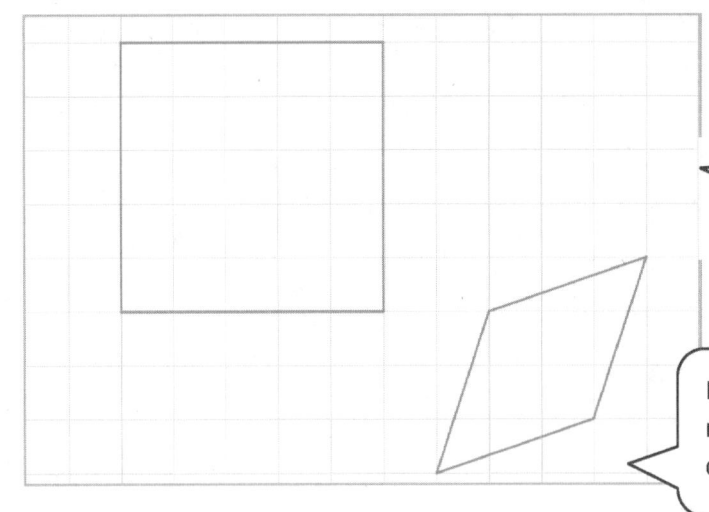

Sample Response:

I created a square.

> I trace the gridlines to draw line segments of equal length, constructing a square.

I created a rhombus.

> I look for a pattern on the grid to draw a rhombus. I draw segments that go diagonally across three squares of the grid.

2. Construct a quadrilateral with two sets of parallel sides. What shape did you create?

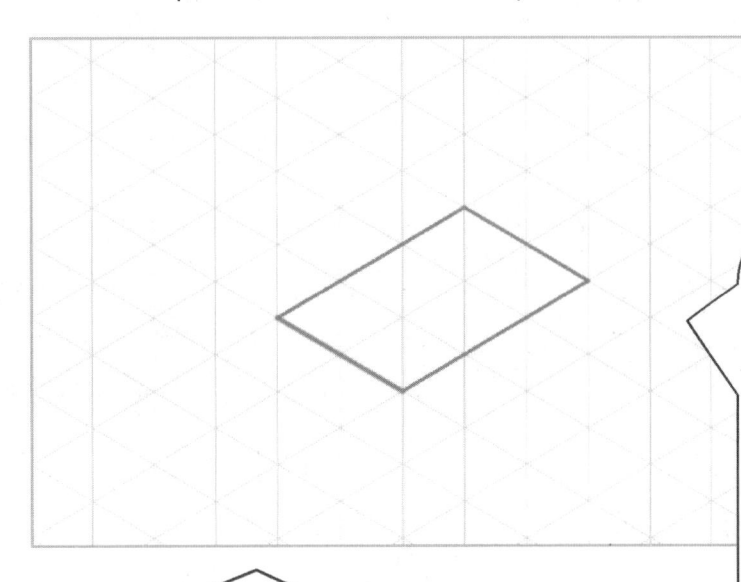

Sample Response:

I created a parallelogram.

> I trace along one of the diagonal gridlines. I draw a second segment parallel to the first by tracing along a gridline two triangle side lengths away. I draw the third and fourth segments by tracing along two other diagonal gridlines going in the opposite direction. I use a ruler and right angle template to verify that the sets of sides are parallel.

> I also could have drawn a rectangle, a square, or a rhombus because they are also parallelograms.

Lesson 16: Reason about attributes to construct quadrilaterals on square or triangular grid paper.

73

A STORY OF UNITS – TEKS EDITION   Lesson 16 Homework 4•4

Name _____   Date _____

Use the grid to construct the following. Name the figure you drew using one of the terms in the word box.

1. Construct a quadrilateral with exactly one set of parallel sides.
   Which shape did you create?

WORD BOX

Parallelogram

Trapezoid

Rectangle

Square

Rhombus

2. Construct a quadrilateral with one set of parallel sides and two right angles.
   Which shape did you create?

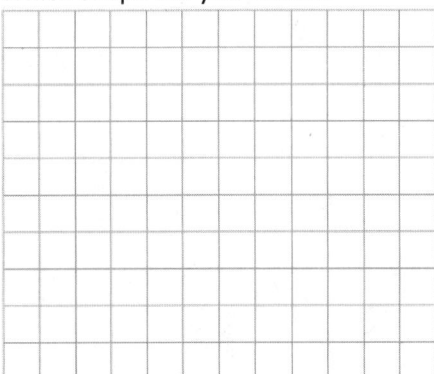

3. Construct a quadrilateral with two sets of parallel sides.
   Which shape did you create?

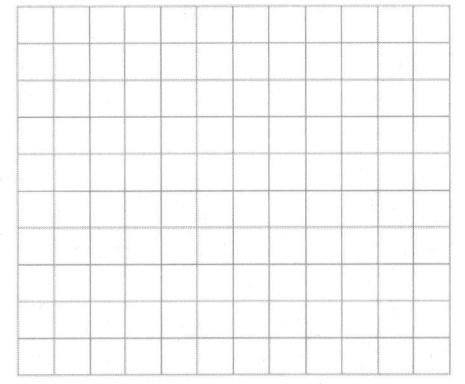

Lesson 16: Reason about attributes to construct quadrilaterals on square or triangular grid paper.

A STORY OF UNITS – TEKS EDITION

Lesson 16 Homework 4•4

4. Construct a quadrilateral with all sides of equal length.
   Which shape did you create?

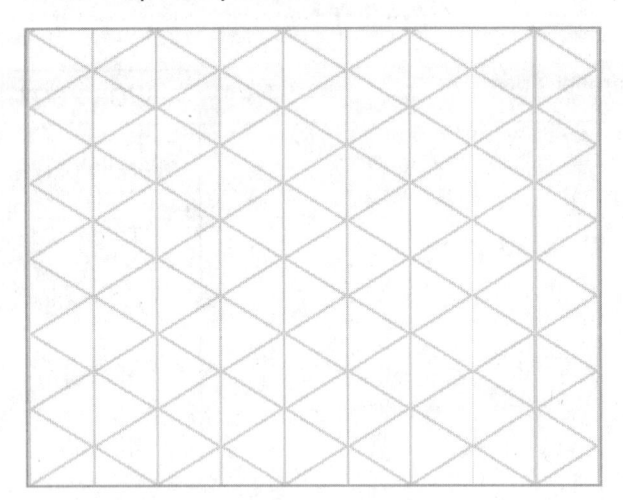

5. Construct a rectangle with all sides of equal length.
   Which shape did you create?

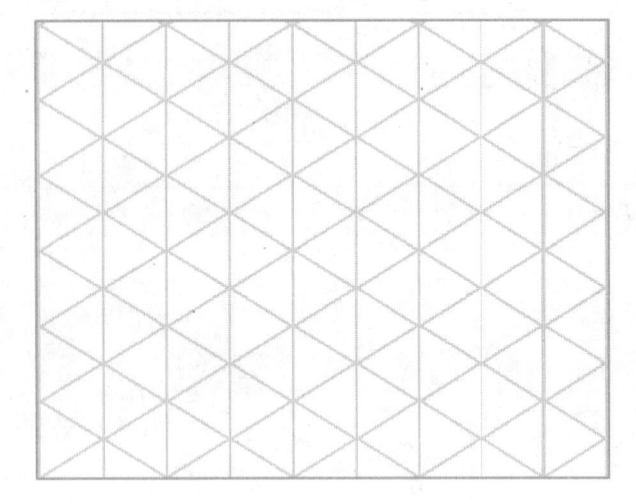

Lesson 16: Reason about attributes to construct quadrilaterals on square or triangular grid paper.

Grade 4
Module 5

A STORY OF UNITS – TEKS EDITION Lesson 1 Homework Helper 4•5

1. Draw a number bond, and write the number sentence to match each strip diagram.

   a.

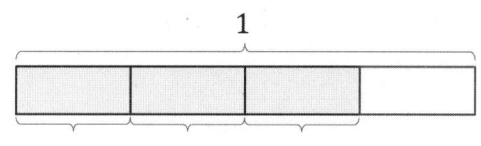

   The rectangle represents 1 and is partitioned into 4 equal units. Each unit is equal to 1 fourth.

   $\frac{3}{4} = \frac{1}{4} + \frac{1}{4} + \frac{1}{4}$

   I can decompose any fraction into unit fractions. 3 fourths is composed of 3 units of 1 fourth.

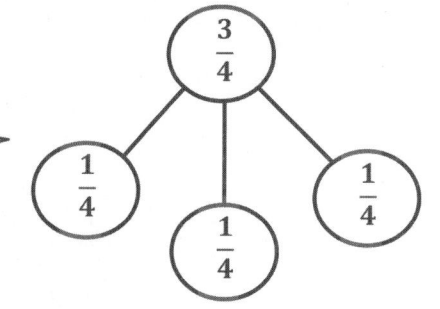

   Number bond: $\frac{3}{4}$ → $\frac{1}{4}$, $\frac{1}{4}$, $\frac{1}{4}$

   b.

   I can rename a fraction greater than 1, such as $\frac{10}{8}$, as a whole number and a fraction, $1\frac{2}{8}$.

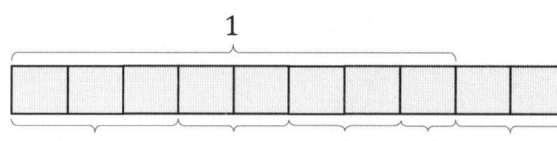

   $\frac{10}{8} = \frac{3}{8} + \frac{2}{8} + \frac{2}{8} + \frac{1}{8} + \frac{2}{8}$

   I know the fractional unit is eighths. I count 8 equal units bracketed as 1 whole.

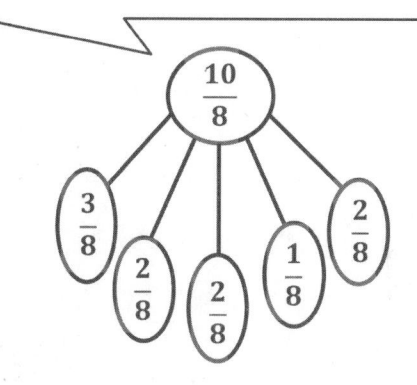

   Number bond: $\frac{10}{8}$ → $\frac{3}{8}$, $\frac{2}{8}$, $\frac{2}{8}$, $\frac{1}{8}$, $\frac{2}{8}$

2. Draw and label strip diagrams to match each number sentence.

   a. $\frac{11}{6} = \frac{3}{6} + \frac{2}{6} + \frac{2}{6} + \frac{4}{6}$

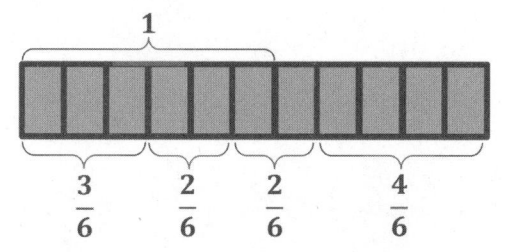

   b. $1\frac{2}{12} = \frac{7}{12} + \frac{4}{12} + \frac{3}{12}$

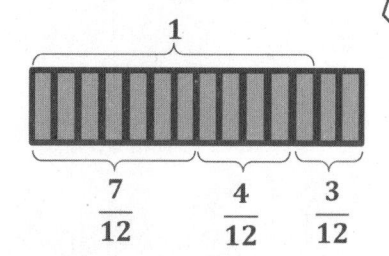

   I know the unit is twelfths. I partition my strip diagram into 12 equal units to represent the whole. I draw 2 more twelfths.

Lesson 1: Decompose fractions as a sum of unit fractions using strip diagrams.

Name _____   Date _____

1. Draw a number bond, and write the number sentence to match each strip diagram. The first one is done for you.

a.

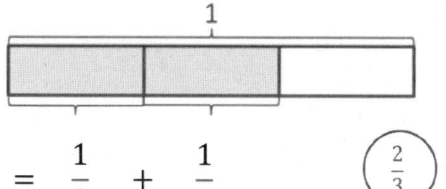

$\dfrac{2}{3} = \dfrac{1}{3} + \dfrac{1}{3}$

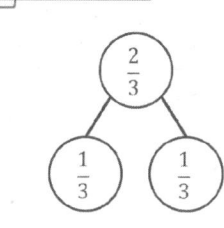

b.

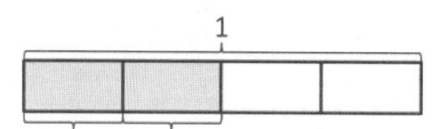

c.

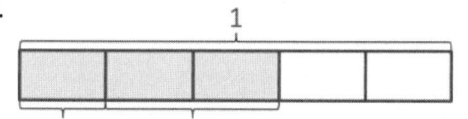

d.

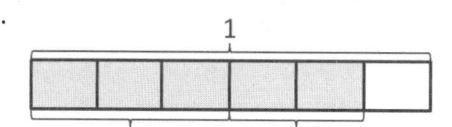

e.

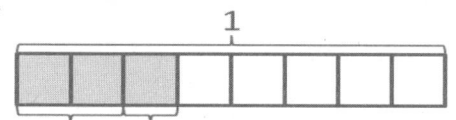

f.

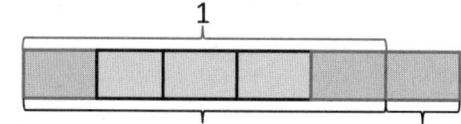

Lesson 1: Decompose fractions as a sum of unit fractions using strip diagrams.

g.

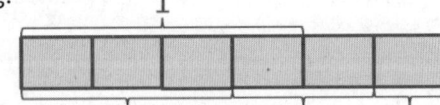

h.

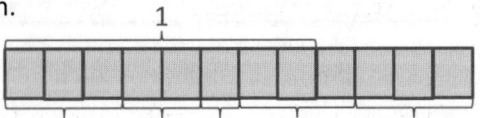

2. Draw and label strip diagrams to match each number sentence.

   a. $\frac{5}{8} = \frac{2}{8} + \frac{2}{8} + \frac{1}{8}$

   b. $\frac{12}{8} = \frac{6}{8} + \frac{2}{8} + \frac{4}{8}$

   c. $\frac{11}{10} = \frac{5}{10} + \frac{5}{10} + \frac{1}{10}$

   d. $\frac{13}{12} = \frac{7}{12} + \frac{1}{12} + \frac{5}{12}$

   e. $1\frac{1}{4} = 1 + \frac{1}{4}$

   f. $1\frac{2}{7} = 1 + \frac{2}{7}$

Lesson 1: Decompose fractions as a sum of unit fractions using strip diagrams.

A STORY OF UNITS – TEKS EDITION | Lesson 2 Homework Helper 4•5

Step 1: Draw and shade a strip diagram of the given fraction.

Step 2: Record the decomposition as a sum of unit fractions.

Step 3: Record the decomposition of the fraction two more ways.

1. $\frac{4}{8}$

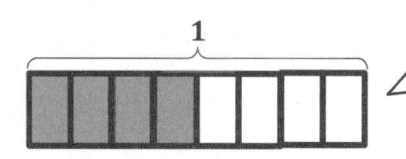

> The bottom number in the fraction determines the fractional size. I draw a whole partitioned into 8 equal parts.

$$\frac{4}{8} = \frac{1}{8} + \frac{1}{8} + \frac{1}{8} + \frac{1}{8}$$

> $\frac{1}{8}$ is a unit fraction because it identifies 1 of the specified fractional size, eighths.

Sample Student Responses:

$$\frac{4}{8} = \frac{2}{8} + \frac{1}{8} + \frac{1}{8} \qquad \frac{4}{8} = \frac{3}{8} + \frac{1}{8}$$

> Adding fractions is like adding whole numbers. Just as 3 ones plus 1 one is 4 ones, 3 eighths plus 1 eighth is 4 eighths.

Step 1: Draw and shade a strip diagram of the given fraction.

Step 2: Record the decomposition of the fraction in three different ways using number sentences.

2. $\frac{8}{5}$ — This fraction is greater than 1.

> 5 fifths is equal to 1.

Sample Student Responses:

$$\frac{8}{5} = 1 + \frac{3}{5} \qquad \frac{8}{5} = \frac{4}{5} + \frac{4}{5} \qquad \frac{8}{5} = \frac{2}{5} + \frac{2}{5} + \frac{3}{5} + \frac{1}{5}$$

Lesson 2: Decompose fractions as a sum of unit fractions using strip diagrams.

Name _____ Date _____

1. Step 1: Draw and shade a strip diagram of the given fraction.
   Step 2: Record the decomposition as a sum of unit fractions.
   Step 3: Record the decomposition of the fraction two more ways.
   (The first one has been done for you.)

   a. $\frac{5}{6}$

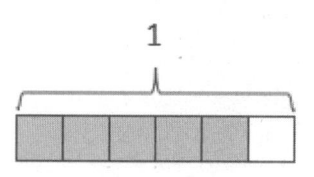

   $\frac{5}{6} = \frac{1}{6} + \frac{1}{6} + \frac{1}{6} + \frac{1}{6} + \frac{1}{6}$ $\qquad$ $\frac{5}{6} = \frac{2}{6} + \frac{2}{6} + \frac{1}{6}$ $\qquad$ $\frac{5}{6} = \frac{1}{6} + \frac{4}{6}$

   b. $\frac{6}{8}$

   c. $\frac{7}{10}$

Lesson 2: Decompose fractions as a sum of unit fractions using strip diagrams.

2. Step 1: Draw and shade a strip diagram of the given fraction.
   Step 2: Record the decomposition of the fraction in three different ways using number sentences.

   a. $\frac{10}{12}$

   b. $\frac{5}{4}$

   c. $\frac{6}{5}$

   d. $1\frac{1}{4}$

A STORY OF UNITS – TEKS EDITION   Lesson 3 Homework Helper   4•5

1. The total length of each strip diagram represents 1. Decompose the shaded unit fractions as the sum of smaller unit fractions in at least two different ways.

   a.

   $\frac{1}{5} = \frac{1}{10} + \frac{1}{10}$

   $\frac{1}{15} + \frac{1}{15} + \frac{1}{15} = \frac{1}{5}$

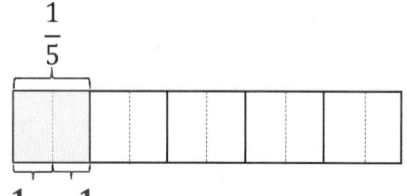

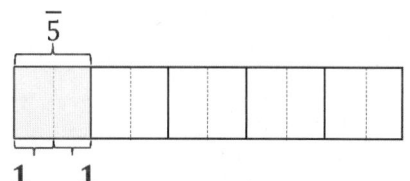

   After decomposing each fifth into 2 equal parts, the new unit is tenths.

   b.

   $\frac{1}{2} = \frac{1}{4} + \frac{1}{4}$

   $\frac{1}{2} = \frac{1}{6} + \frac{1}{6} + \frac{1}{6}$

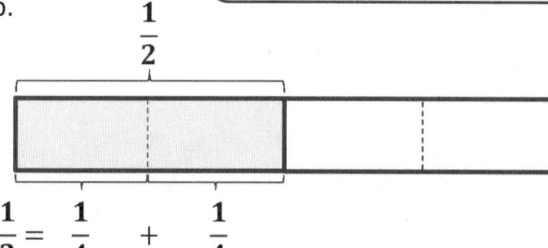

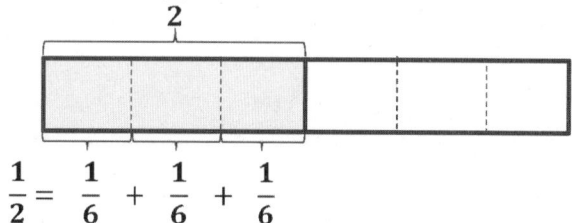

2. Draw a strip diagram to prove $\frac{2}{3} = \frac{4}{6}$.

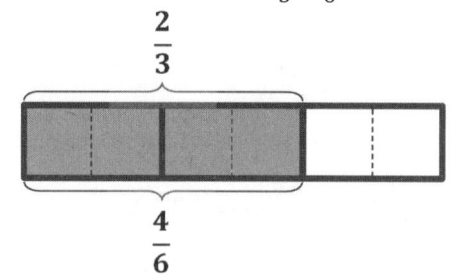

   I know that $\frac{2}{3}$ and $\frac{4}{6}$ are equal because they take up the same amount of space.

3. Show that $\frac{1}{2}$ is equivalent to $\frac{4}{8}$ using a strip diagram and a number sentence.

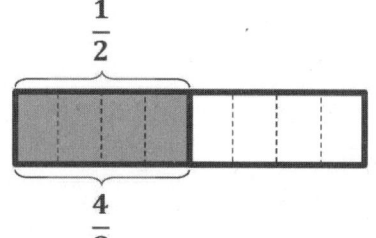

   $\frac{1}{2} = \frac{1}{8} + \frac{1}{8} + \frac{1}{8} + \frac{1}{8}$

   I know that $\frac{1}{2}$ and $\frac{4}{8}$ are equivalent because four $\frac{1}{8}$-sized pieces are equal to one $\frac{1}{2}$-sized piece.

Lesson 3: Decompose fractions into sums of smaller unit fractions using strip diagrams.

Name _____   Date _____

1. The total length of each strip diagram represents 1. Decompose the shaded unit fractions as the sum of smaller unit fractions in at least two different ways. The first one has been done for you.

   a.

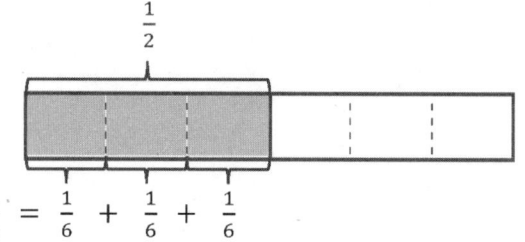

   $\frac{1}{2} = \frac{1}{6} + \frac{1}{6} + \frac{1}{6}$

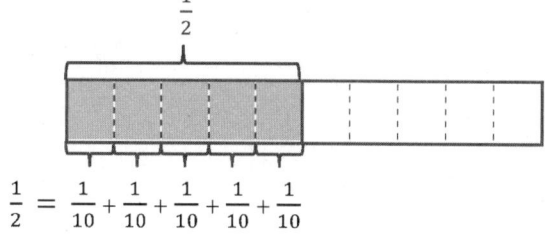

   $\frac{1}{2} = \frac{1}{10} + \frac{1}{10} + \frac{1}{10} + \frac{1}{10} + \frac{1}{10}$

   b.

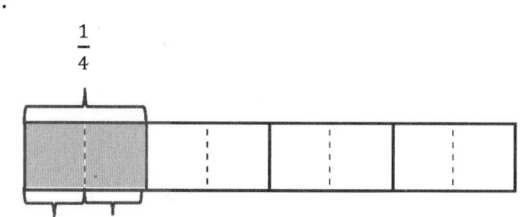

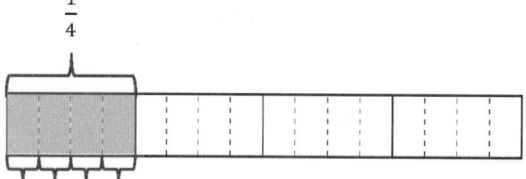

2. The total length of each strip diagram represents 1. Decompose the shaded fractions as the sum of smaller unit fractions in at least two different ways.

   a.

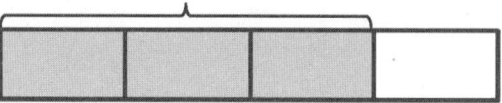

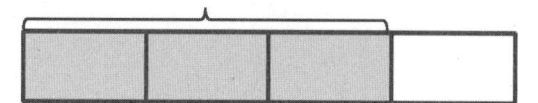

   b.

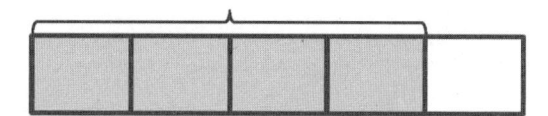

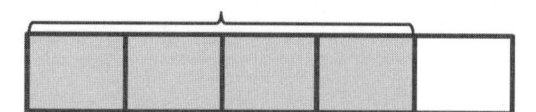

Lesson 3: Decompose fractions into sums of smaller unit fractions using strip diagrams.

c.

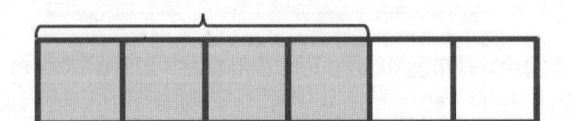

3. Draw strip diagrams to prove the following statements. The first one has been done for you.

   a. $\frac{2}{5} = \frac{4}{10}$

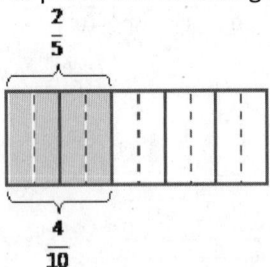

   b. $\frac{3}{6} = \frac{6}{12}$

   c. $\frac{2}{6} = \frac{6}{18}$

   d. $\frac{3}{4} = \frac{12}{16}$

4. Show that $\frac{1}{2}$ is equivalent to $\frac{6}{12}$ using a strip diagram and a number sentence.

5. Show that $\frac{2}{3}$ is equivalent to $\frac{8}{12}$ using a strip diagram and a number sentence.

6. Show that $\frac{4}{5}$ is equivalent to $\frac{12}{15}$ using a strip diagram and a number sentence.

A STORY OF UNITS – TEKS EDITION   Lesson 4 Homework Helper   4•5

1. Draw horizontal line(s) to decompose the rectangle into 2 rows. Use the model to name the shaded area as a sum of unit fractions.

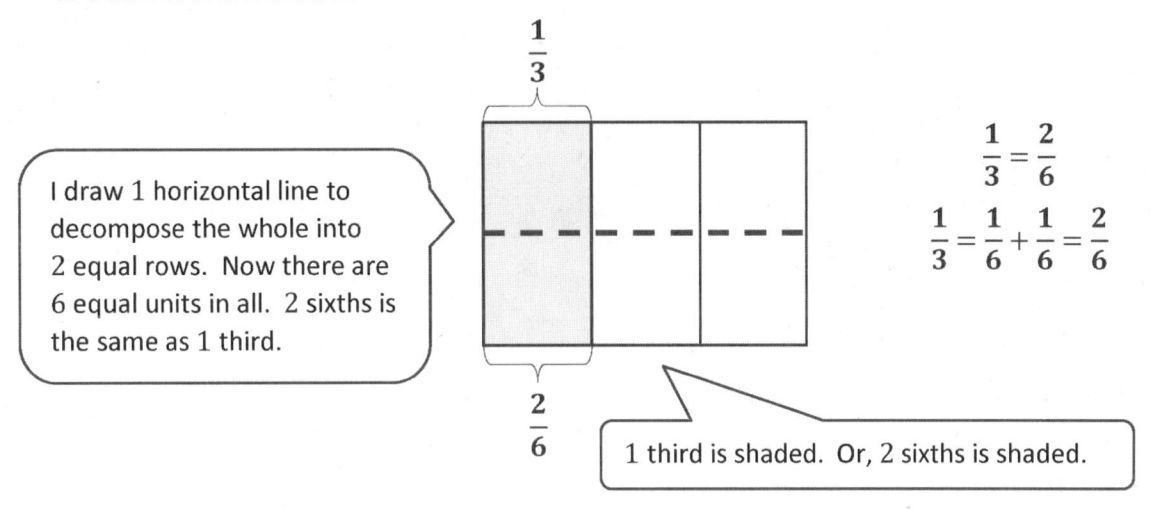

I draw 1 horizontal line to decompose the whole into 2 equal rows. Now there are 6 equal units in all. 2 sixths is the same as 1 third.

$$\frac{1}{3} = \frac{2}{6}$$

$$\frac{1}{3} = \frac{1}{6} + \frac{1}{6} = \frac{2}{6}$$

1 third is shaded. Or, 2 sixths is shaded.

2. Draw area models to show the decompositions represented by the number sentences below. Represent the decomposition as a sum of unit fractions.

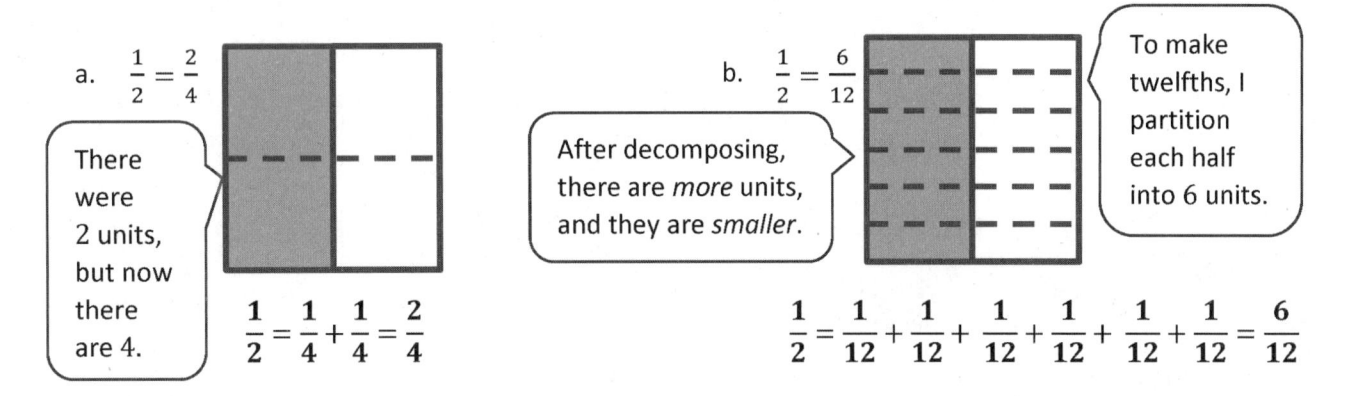

a. $\frac{1}{2} = \frac{2}{4}$

There were 2 units, but now there are 4.

$$\frac{1}{2} = \frac{1}{4} + \frac{1}{4} = \frac{2}{4}$$

b. $\frac{1}{2} = \frac{6}{12}$

After decomposing, there are *more* units, and they are *smaller*.

To make twelfths, I partition each half into 6 units.

$$\frac{1}{2} = \frac{1}{12} + \frac{1}{12} + \frac{1}{12} + \frac{1}{12} + \frac{1}{12} + \frac{1}{12} = \frac{6}{12}$$

3. Explain why $\frac{1}{12} + \frac{1}{12} + \frac{1}{12} + \frac{1}{12} + \frac{1}{12} + \frac{1}{12}$ is the same as $\frac{1}{2}$.

Sample Student Response:

I see in the area model that I drew that 6 twelfths takes up the same space as 1 half. 6 twelfths and 1 half have exactly the same area.

Lesson 4: Decompose unit fractions using area models to show equivalence.

A STORY OF UNITS – TEKS EDITION   Lesson 4 Homework 4•5

Name _____   Date _____

1. Draw horizontal lines to decompose each rectangle into the number of rows as indicated. Use the model to give the shaded area as a sum of unit fractions.

   a. 3 rows

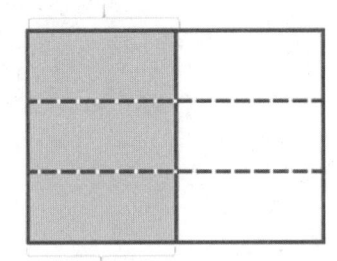

   $$\frac{1}{2} = \frac{3}{-}$$

   $$\frac{1}{2} = \frac{1}{6} + \frac{-}{-} + \frac{-}{-} = \frac{3}{6}$$

   b. 2 rows

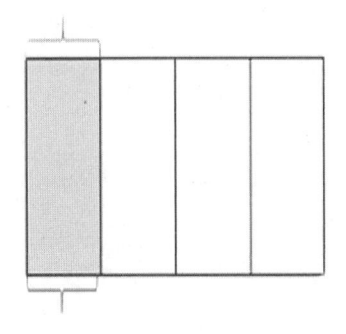

   c. 4 rows

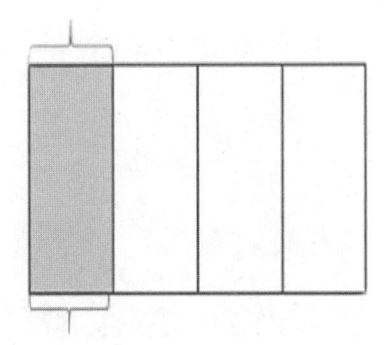

   Lesson 4: Decompose unit fractions using area models to show equivalence.

2. Draw area models to show the decompositions represented by the number sentences below. Represent the decomposition as a sum of unit fractions.

   a. $\frac{1}{3} = \frac{2}{6}$

   b. $\frac{1}{3} = \frac{3}{9}$

   c. $\frac{1}{3} = \frac{4}{12}$

   d. $\frac{1}{3} = \frac{5}{15}$

   e. $\frac{1}{5} = \frac{2}{10}$

   f. $\frac{1}{5} = \frac{3}{15}$

3. Explain why $\frac{1}{12} + \frac{1}{12} + \frac{1}{12} + \frac{1}{12}$ is the same as $\frac{1}{3}$.

A STORY OF UNITS – TEKS EDITION — Lesson 5 Homework Helper — 4•5

1. The rectangle represents 1. Draw horizontal line(s) to decompose the rectangle into *twelfths*. Use the model to name the shaded area as a sum of unit fractions. Use parentheses to show the relationship between the number sentences.

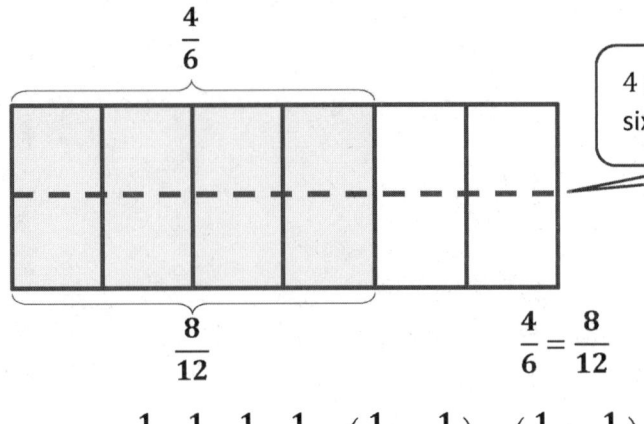

$\frac{4}{6}$

> 4 sixths are shaded. I draw one line to partition sixths into twelfths. 8 twelfths are shaded.

$\frac{8}{12}$

$\frac{4}{6} = \frac{8}{12}$

> I write addition sentences using unit fractions.

$\frac{1}{6} + \frac{1}{6} + \frac{1}{6} + \frac{1}{6} = \left(\frac{1}{12} + \frac{1}{12}\right) + \left(\frac{1}{12} + \frac{1}{12}\right) + \left(\frac{1}{12} + \frac{1}{12}\right) + \left(\frac{1}{12} + \frac{1}{12}\right) = \frac{8}{12}$

2. Draw an area model to show the decompositions represented by $\frac{2}{3} = \frac{6}{9}$. Express $\frac{2}{3} = \frac{6}{9}$ as a sum of unit fractions. Use parentheses to show the relationship between the number sentences.

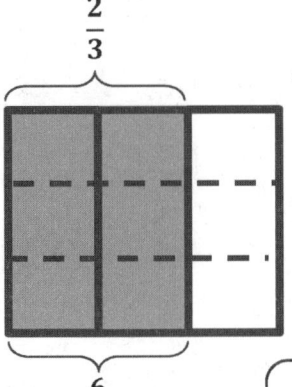

$\frac{2}{3}$

> I draw thirds vertically and partition the thirds into ninths with two horizontal lines.

$\frac{6}{9}$

$\frac{2}{3} = \frac{6}{9}$

$\frac{1}{3} + \frac{1}{3} = \left(\frac{1}{9} + \frac{1}{9} + \frac{1}{9}\right) + \left(\frac{1}{9} + \frac{1}{9} + \frac{1}{9}\right) = \frac{6}{9}$

> I write parentheses that show the decomposition of $\frac{1}{3}$. Just as the area model shows 1 third partitioned into 3 ninths, so do the parentheses.

Lesson 5: Decompose fractions using area models to show equivalence.

Name _____   Date _____

1. Each rectangle represents 1. Draw horizontal lines to decompose each rectangle into the fractional units as indicated. Use the model to give the shaded area as a sum of unit fractions. Use parentheses to show the relationship between the number sentences. The first one has been partially done for you.

   a. Tenths

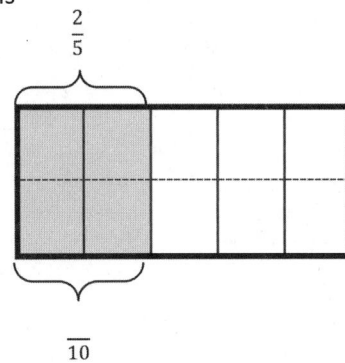

   $\frac{2}{5} = \frac{4}{\_\_}$

   $\frac{\_}{5} + \frac{\_}{5} = \left(\frac{1}{10} + \frac{1}{10}\right) + \left(\frac{1}{10} + \frac{1}{10}\right) = \frac{4}{\_\_}$

   b. Eighths

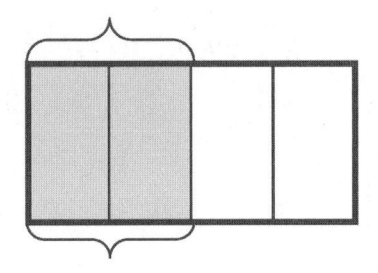

Lesson 5: Decompose fractions using area models to show equivalence.

c. Fifteenths

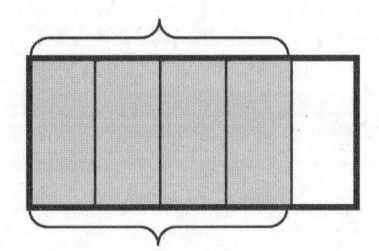

2. Draw area models to show the decompositions represented by the number sentences below. Express each as a sum of unit fractions. Use parentheses to show the relationship between the number sentences.

   a. $\frac{2}{3} = \frac{4}{6}$

   b. $\frac{4}{5} = \frac{8}{10}$

Lesson 5: Decompose fractions using area models to show equivalence.

3. Step 1: Draw an area model for a fraction with units of thirds, fourths, or fifths.

   Step 2: Shade in more than one fractional unit.

   Step 3: Partition the area model again to find an equivalent fraction.

   Step 4: Write the equivalent fractions as a number sentence. (If you have written a number sentence like this one already in this Homework, start over.)

A STORY OF UNITS – TEKS EDITION · Lesson 6 Homework Helper · 4•5

Each rectangle represents 1.

1. The shaded unit fractions have been decomposed into smaller units. Express the equivalent fractions in a number sentence using multiplication.

   a.

   $$\frac{1}{3} = \frac{1 \times 2}{3 \times 2} = \frac{2}{6}$$

   > The numerator is 1.
   > The denominator is 3.

   b.

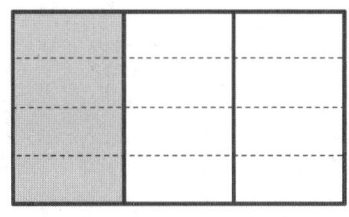

   $$\frac{1}{3} = \frac{1 \times 4}{3 \times 4} = \frac{4}{12}$$

   > I can multiply the numerator (number of fractional units selected) and the denominator (the fractional unit) by 4 to make an equivalent fraction.

2. Decompose the shaded fraction into smaller units using the area model. Express the equivalent fractions in a number sentence using multiplication.

   > The area model shows that $\frac{1}{6}$ equals $\frac{3}{18}$.

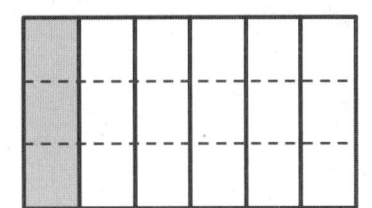

   > As I multiply, the size of the units gets smaller.

   $$\frac{1}{6} = \frac{1 \times 3}{6 \times 3} = \frac{3}{18}$$

3. Draw three different area models to represent 1 half by shading.

   Decompose the shaded fraction into (a) fourths, (b) sixths, and (c) eighths.

   Use multiplication to show how each fraction is equivalent to 1 half.

   a.

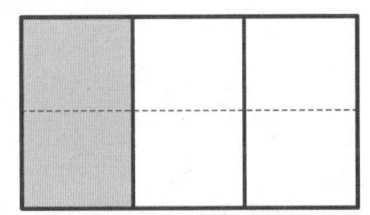

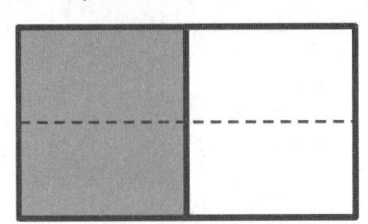

   $$\frac{1}{2} = \frac{1 \times 2}{2 \times 2} = \frac{2}{4}$$

   > The number of units doubled.

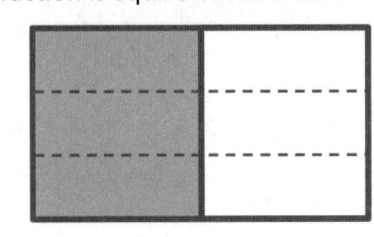

   b.

   $$\frac{1}{2} = \frac{1 \times 3}{2 \times 3} = \frac{3}{6}$$

   > The number of units tripled.

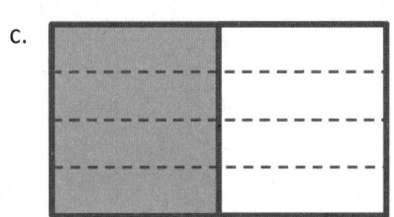

   c.

   $$\frac{1}{2} = \frac{1 \times 4}{2 \times 4} = \frac{4}{8}$$

   > The number of units quadrupled.

Lesson 6: Use the area model and multiplication to show the equivalence of two fractions.

A STORY OF UNITS – TEKS EDITION

Lesson 6 Homework 4•5

Name _____ Date _____

Each rectangle represents 1.

1. The shaded unit fractions have been decomposed into smaller units. Express the equivalent fractions in a number sentence using multiplication. The first one has been done for you.

   a.

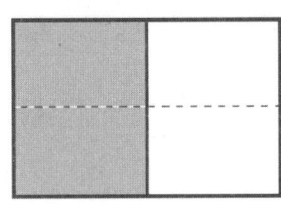

   $$\frac{1}{2} = \frac{1 \times 2}{2 \times 2} = \frac{2}{4}$$

   b.

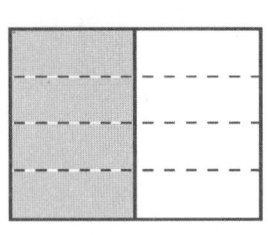

   c.

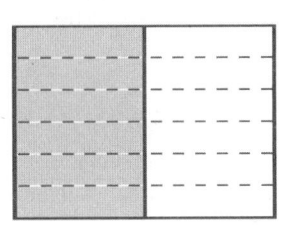

   d.

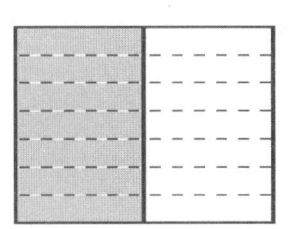

2. Decompose the shaded fractions into smaller units using the area models. Express the equivalent fractions in a number sentence using multiplication.

   a.

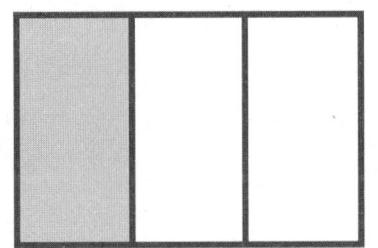

   b.

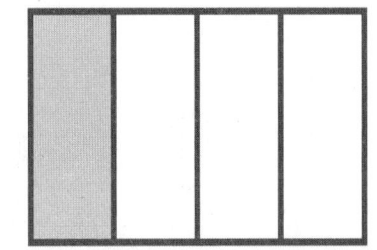

Lesson 6: Use the area model and multiplication to show the equivalence of two fractions.

105

c.

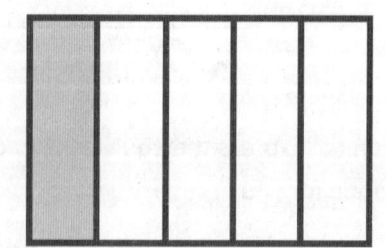

d.

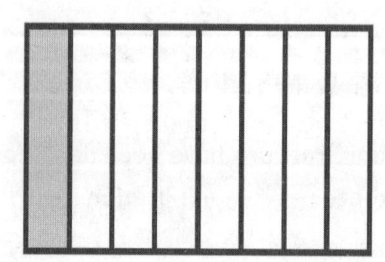

3. Draw three different area models to represent 1 fourth by shading.
Decompose the shaded fraction into (a) eighths, (b) twelfths, and (c) sixteenths.
Use multiplication to show how each fraction is equivalent to 1 fourth.

a.

b.

c.

Lesson 6: Use the area model and multiplication to show the equivalence of two fractions.

A STORY OF UNITS – TEKS EDITION   Lesson 7 Homework Helper   4•5

Each rectangle represents 1.

1. The shaded fraction has been decomposed into smaller units. Express the equivalent fraction in a number sentence using multiplication.

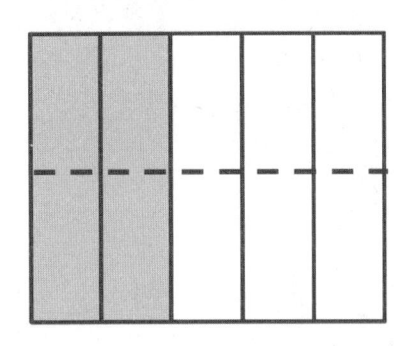

$$\frac{2}{5} = \frac{2 \times 2}{5 \times 2} = \frac{4}{10}$$

The number of units in the area model has been doubled. There were 5 units, and now there are 10 units.

2. Decompose both shaded fractions into sixteenths. Express the equivalent fractions in a number sentence using multiplication.

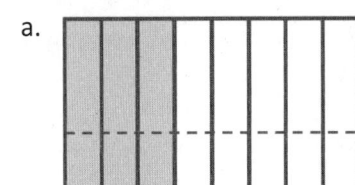

a.
$$\frac{3}{8} = \frac{3 \times 2}{8 \times 2} = \frac{6}{16}$$

I draw 1 line to partition each unit into 2.

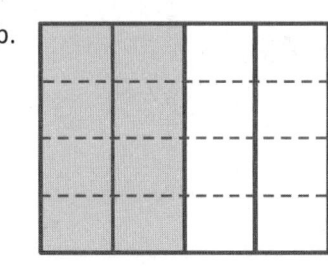

b.
$$\frac{2}{4} = \frac{2 \times 4}{4 \times 4} = \frac{8}{16}$$

I draw 3 lines to partition each unit into 4.

3. Use multiplication to create an equivalent fraction for the fraction $\frac{8}{6}$.

$$\frac{8}{6} = \frac{8 \times 2}{6 \times 2} = \frac{16}{12}$$

To make an equivalent fraction, I can choose any fraction equivalent to 1. I can choose $\frac{3}{3}, \frac{4}{4}, \frac{5}{5}$, etc.

4. Determine if the following is a true number sentence. Correct it if it is false by changing the right-hand side of the number sentence.

$$\frac{5}{4} = \frac{15}{16}$$

This is false! The numerator was multiplied by 3. The denominator was multiplied by 4. Three fourths is not a fraction equal to 1.

Sample Student Response:

Not true!

$$\frac{5}{4} = \frac{5 \times 3}{4 \times 3} = \frac{15}{12}$$

Lesson 7: Use the area model and multiplication to show the equivalence of two fractions.

107

Name _____ Date _____

Each rectangle represents 1.

1. The shaded fractions have been decomposed into smaller units. Express the equivalent fractions in a number sentence using multiplication. The first one has been done for you.

   a.

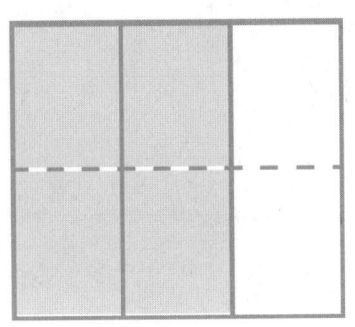

   $$\frac{2}{3} = \frac{2 \times 2}{3 \times 2} = \frac{4}{6}$$

   b.

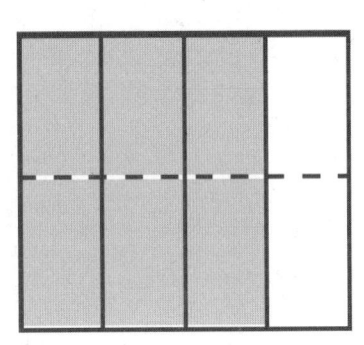

   c.

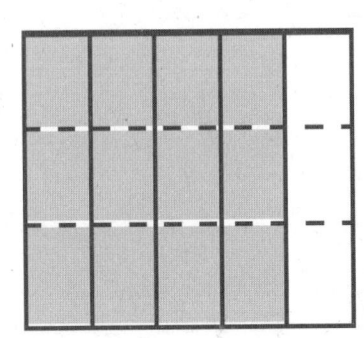

   d.

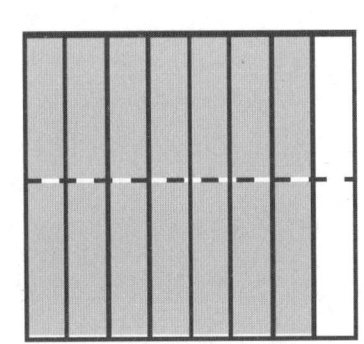

2. Decompose both shaded fractions into twelfths. Express the equivalent fractions in a number sentence using multiplication.

   a.

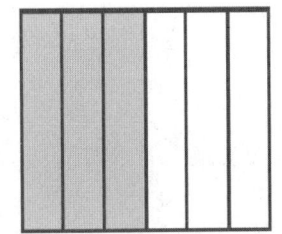

   b.

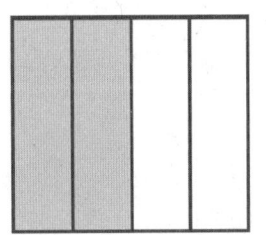

Lesson 7: Use the area model and multiplication to show the equivalence of two fractions.

3. Draw area models to prove that the following number sentences are true.

   a. $\frac{1}{3} = \frac{2}{6}$

   b. $\frac{2}{5} = \frac{4}{10}$

   c. $\frac{5}{7} = \frac{10}{14}$

   d. $\frac{3}{6} = \frac{9}{18}$

4. Use multiplication to create an equivalent fraction for each fraction below.

   a. $\frac{2}{3}$

   b. $\frac{5}{6}$

   c. $\frac{6}{5}$

   d. $\frac{10}{8}$

5. Determine which of the following are true number sentences. Correct those that are false by changing the right-hand side of the number sentence.

   a. $\frac{2}{3} = \frac{4}{9}$

   b. $\frac{5}{6} = \frac{10}{12}$

   c. $\frac{3}{5} = \frac{6}{15}$

   d. $\frac{7}{4} = \frac{21}{12}$

A STORY OF UNITS – TEKS EDITION

Lesson 8 Homework Helper 4•5

Each rectangle represents 1.

1. Compose the shaded fraction into larger fractional units. Express the equivalent fractions in a number sentence using division.

   a.

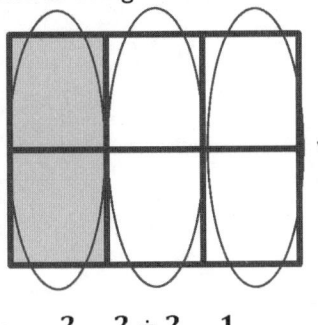

   $$\frac{2}{6} = \frac{2 \div 2}{6 \div 2} = \frac{1}{3}$$

   > 2 units are shaded. I make groups of 2. Sixths are composed as thirds.

   > I divide the numerator and denominator by 2.

   b.

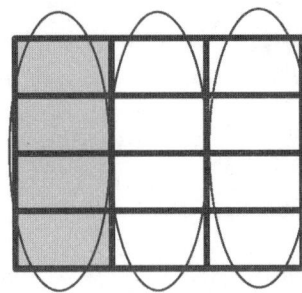

   $$\frac{4}{12} = \frac{4 \div 4}{12 \div 4} = \frac{1}{3}$$

   > When I compose thirds, the number of units decreases. I make a larger unit.

2.
   a. In the first model, show 2 tenths. In the second area model, show 3 fifteenths. Show how both fractions can be composed, or renamed, as the same unit fraction.

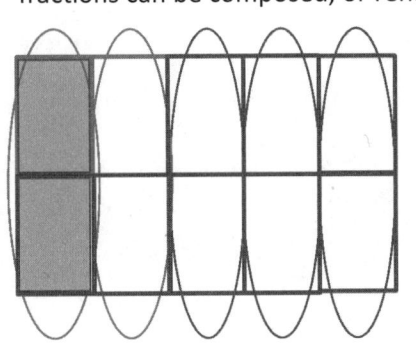

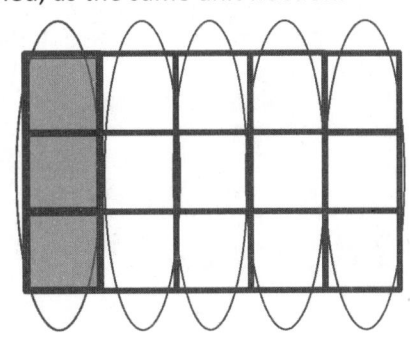

   2 tenths = 1 fifth   3 fifteenths = 1 fifth

   > Before I draw my model, I identify the larger unit fraction. I know 3 fifteenths is the same as $\frac{1 \times 3}{5 \times 3}$.

   b. Express the equivalent fractions in a number sentence using division.

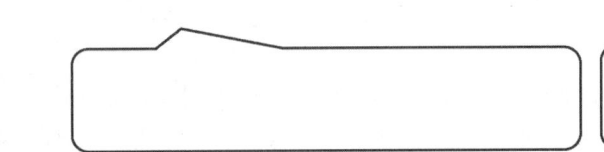

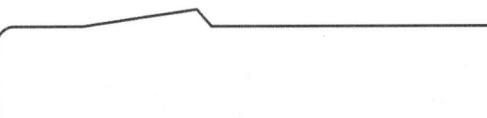

Lesson 8: Use the area model and division to show the equivalence of two fractions.

111

A STORY OF UNITS – TEKS EDITION

Lesson 8 Homework 4•5

Name _____ Date _____

Each rectangle represents 1.

1. Compose the shaded fractions into larger fractional units. Express the equivalent fractions in a number sentence using division. The first one has been done for you.

   a.

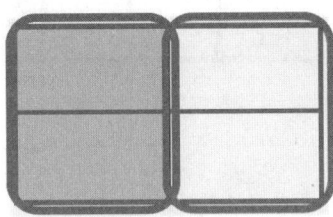

   $$\frac{2}{4} = \frac{2 \div 2}{4 \div 2} = \frac{1}{2}$$

   b.

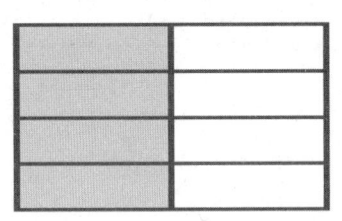

   c.

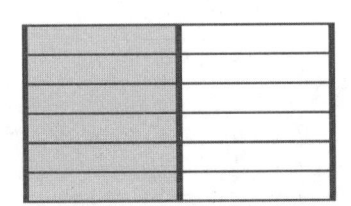

   d.

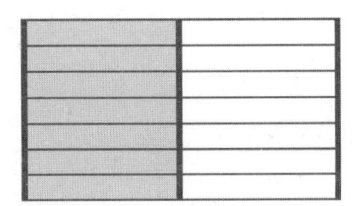

Lesson 8: Use the area model and division to show the equivalence of two fractions.

2. Compose the shaded fractions into larger fractional units. Express the equivalent fractions in a number sentence using division.

   a.

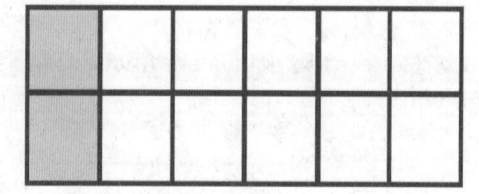

   b.

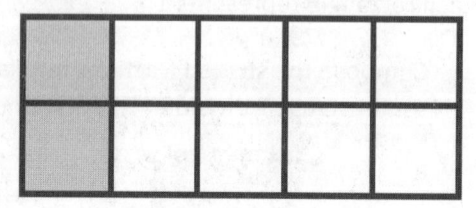

   c.

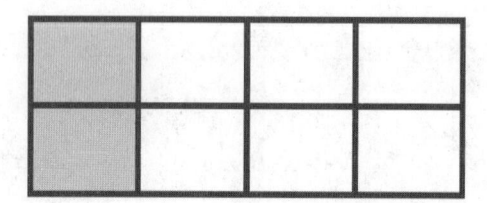

   d.

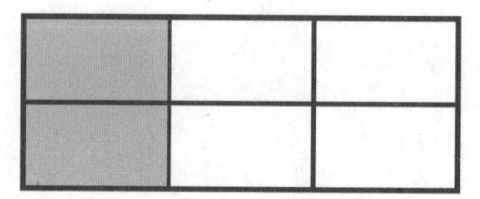

   e. What happened to the size of the fractional units when you composed the fraction?

   f. What happened to the total number of units in the whole when you composed the fraction?

3. a. In the first area model, show 4 eighths. In the second area model, show 6 twelfths. Show how both fractions can be composed, or renamed, as the same unit fraction.

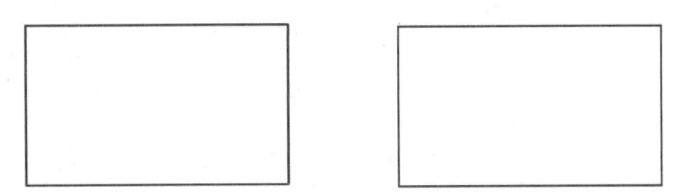

   b. Express the equivalent fractions in a number sentence using division.

4. a. In the first area model, show 4 eighths. In the second area model, show 8 sixteenths. Show how both fractions can be composed, or renamed, as the same unit fraction.

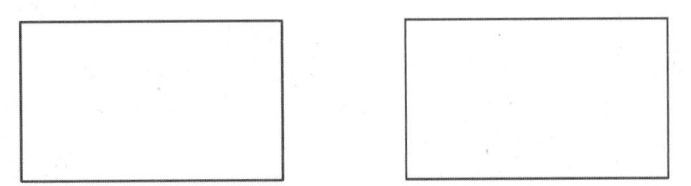

   b. Express the equivalent fractions in a number sentence using division.

Lesson 8: Use the area model and division to show the equivalence of two fractions.

A STORY OF UNITS – TEKS EDITION

Lesson 9 Homework Helper   4•5

Each rectangle represents 1.

1. Compose the shaded fraction into larger fractional units. Express the equivalent fractions in a number sentence using division.

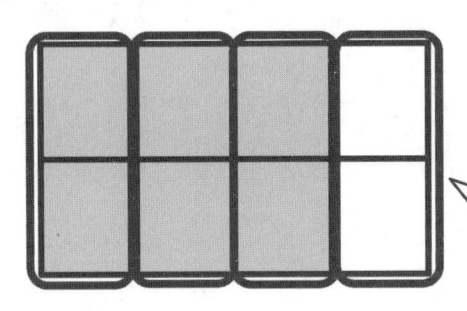

$$\frac{6}{8} = \frac{6 \div 2}{8 \div 2} = \frac{3}{4}$$

> This work is a lot like what I did in Lesson 9. However, once I compose units, the renamed fraction is not a unit fraction.

2. Draw an area model to represent the number sentence below.

$$\frac{4}{14} = \frac{4 \div 2}{14 \div 2} = \frac{2}{7}$$

> Looking at the numerator and denominator, I draw 14 units and shade 4 units.

> Looking at the divisor, $\frac{2}{2}$, I circle groups of 2. I make 7 groups. 2 sevenths are shaded.

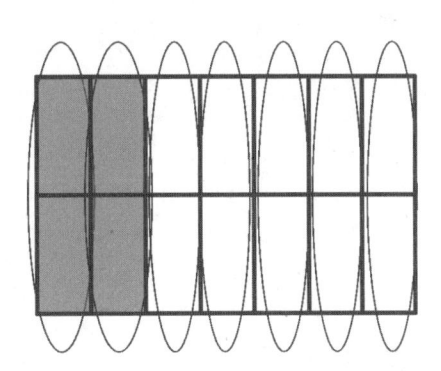

3. Use division to rename the fraction below. Draw a model if that helps you. See if you can use the largest common factor.

$$\frac{8}{20} = \frac{8 \div 4}{20 \div 4} = \frac{2}{5}$$

> I could choose 2, but the largest common factor is 4.

> Whether I compose units vertically or horizontally, I get the same answer!

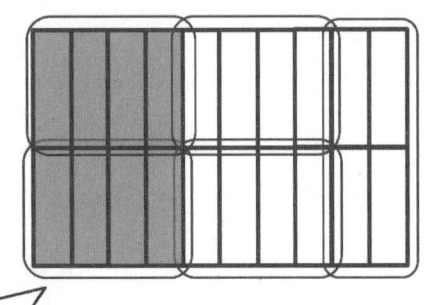

Lesson 9: Use the area model and division to show the equivalence of two fractions.

117

Name _____   Date _____

Each rectangle represents 1.

1. Compose the shaded fraction into larger fractional units. Express the equivalent fractions in a number sentence using division. The first one has been done for you.

   a.

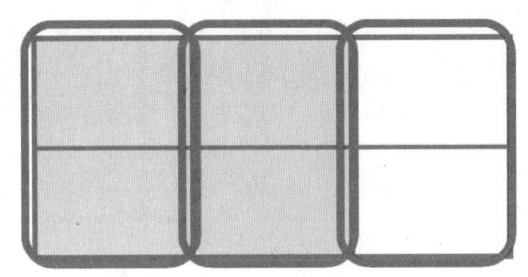

   $$\frac{4}{6} = \frac{4 \div 2}{6 \div 2} = \frac{2}{3}$$

   b.

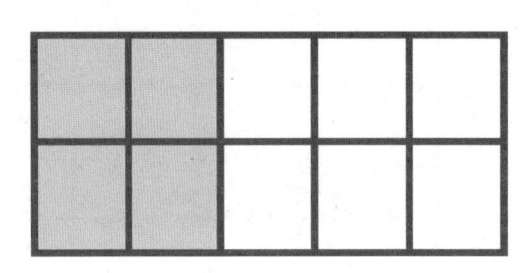

   c.

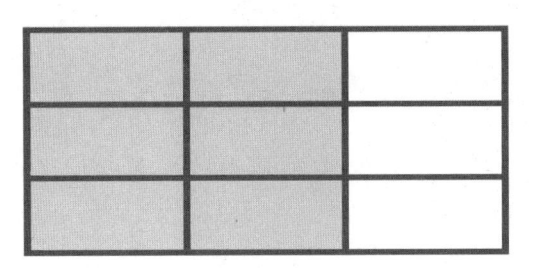

   d.

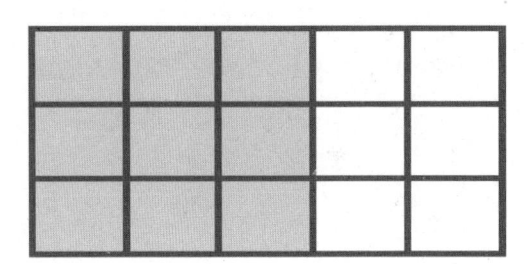

Lesson 9: Use the area model and division to show the equivalence of two fractions.

2. Compose the shaded fractions into larger fractional units. Express the equivalent fractions in a number sentence using division.

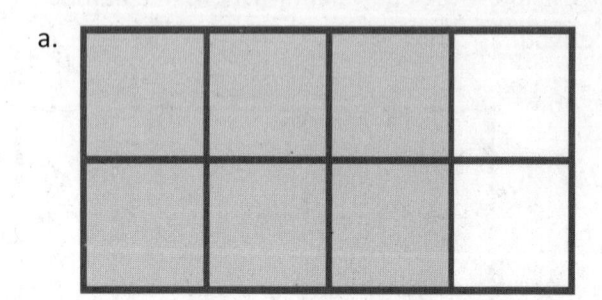

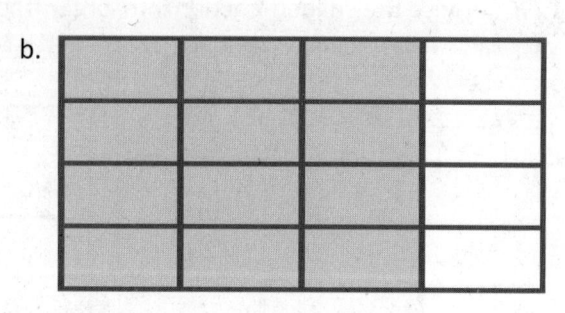

   a.

   b.

3. Draw an area model to represent each number sentence below.

   a. $\frac{6}{15} = \frac{6 \div 3}{15 \div 3} = \frac{2}{5}$

   b. $\frac{6}{18} = \frac{6 \div 3}{18 \div 3} = \frac{2}{6}$

4. Use division to rename each fraction given below. Draw a model if that helps you. See if you can use the largest common factor.

   a. $\frac{6}{12}$

   b. $\frac{4}{12}$

   c. $\frac{8}{12}$

   d. $\frac{12}{18}$

A STORY OF UNITS – TEKS EDITION   Lesson 10 Homework Helper   4•5

1. Label each number line with the fractions shown on the strip diagram. Circle the fraction that labels the point on the number line and also names the shaded part of the strip diagram.

   a.

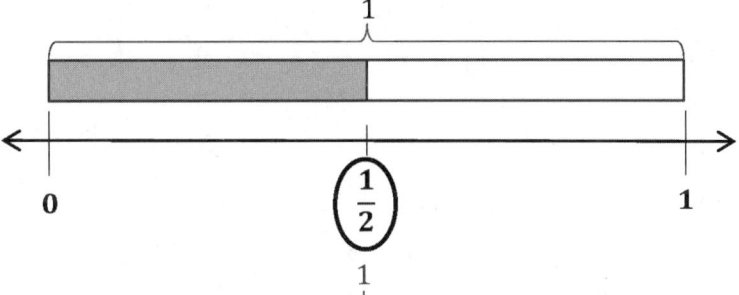

   0   (1/2)   1

   b.

   0   1/4   (2/4)   3/4   1

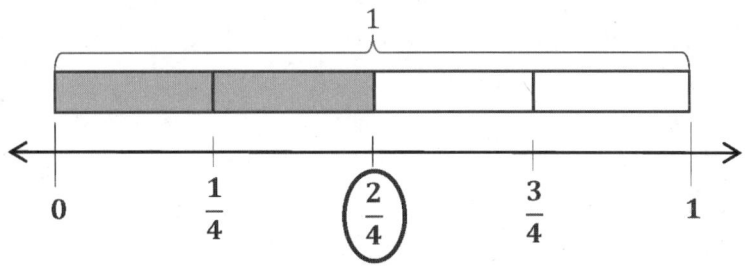

   > The number line and strip diagram show that $\frac{2}{4}$ is equivalent to $\frac{1}{2}$.

2. Write number sentences using multiplication to show the fraction represented in 1(a) is equivalent to the fraction represented in 1(b).

   $$\frac{1}{2} = \frac{1 \times 2}{2 \times 2} = \frac{2}{4}$$

3. a. Partition a number line from 0 to 1 into thirds. Decompose $\frac{2}{3}$ into 4 equal lengths.

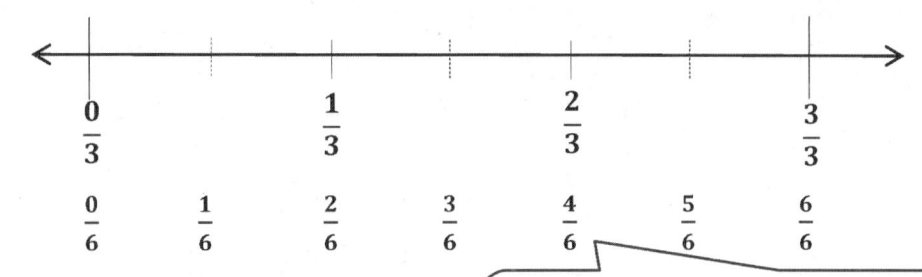

   $\frac{0}{3}$ $\frac{1}{3}$ $\frac{2}{3}$ $\frac{3}{3}$

   $\frac{0}{6}$ $\frac{1}{6}$ $\frac{2}{6}$ $\frac{3}{6}$ $\frac{4}{6}$ $\frac{5}{6}$ $\frac{6}{6}$

   > To decompose 2 thirds into 4 equal parts, each unit is partitioned into two. To name the new, smaller units, I decompose each third. Thirds become sixths, so $\frac{2}{3} = \frac{4}{6}$.

Lesson 10: Explain fraction equivalence using a strip diagram and the number line, and relate that to the use of multiplication and division.

c. Write 1 multiplication and 1 division sentence to show what fraction represented on the number line is equivalent to $\frac{2}{3}$.

$$\frac{2}{3} = \frac{2 \times 2}{3 \times 2} = \frac{4}{6} \qquad \frac{4}{6} = \frac{4 \div 2}{6 \div 2} = \frac{2}{3}$$

A STORY OF UNITS – TEKS EDITION Lesson 10 Homework 4•5

Name _____ Date _____

1. Label each number line with the fractions shown on the strip diagram. Circle the fraction that labels the point on the number line that also names the shaded part of the strip diagram.

   a.

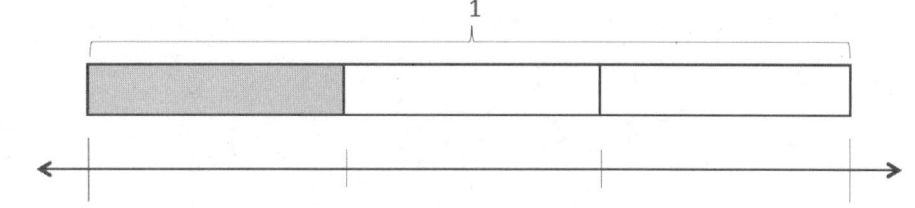

   b.

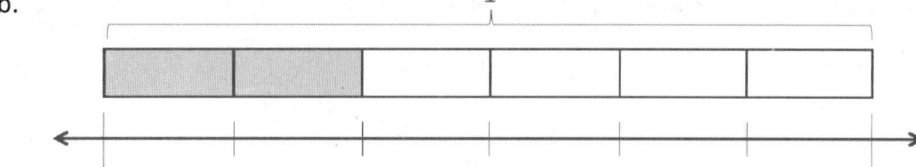

   c.

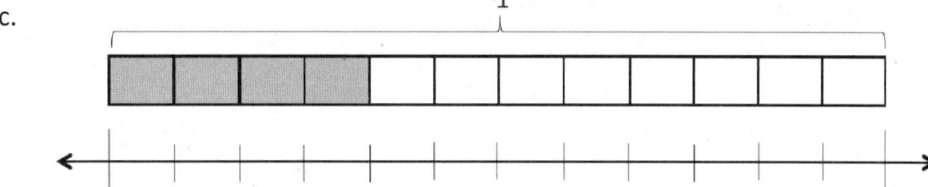

Lesson 10: Explain fraction equivalence using a strip diagram and the number line, and relate that to the use of multiplication and division.

2. Write number sentences using multiplication to show:
   a. The fraction represented in 1(a) is equivalent to the fraction represented in 1(b).

   b. The fraction represented in 1(a) is equivalent to the fraction represented in 1(c).

3. Use each shaded strip diagram below as a ruler to draw a number line. Mark each number line with the fractional units shown on the strip diagram, and circle the fraction that labels the point on the number line that also names the shaded part of the strip diagram.

   a.

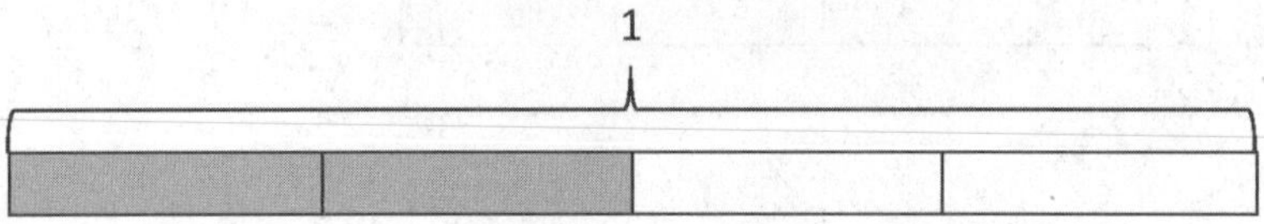

   b.

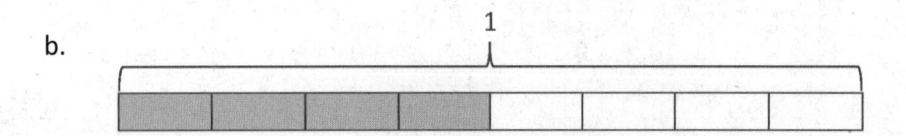

   c.

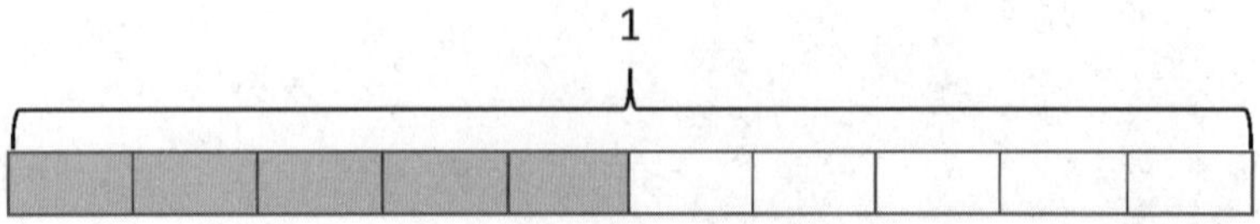

4. Write a number sentence using division to show the fraction represented in 3(a) is equivalent to the fraction represented in 3(b).

5. a. Partition a number line from 0 to 1 into fourths. Decompose $\frac{3}{4}$ into 6 equal lengths.

   b. Write a number sentence using multiplication to show what fraction represented on the number line is equivalent to $\frac{3}{4}$.

   c. Write a number sentence using division to show what fraction represented on the number line is equivalent to $\frac{3}{4}$.

A STORY OF UNITS – TEKS EDITION   Lesson 11 Homework Helper   4•5

1.
   a. Plot the following points on the number line without measuring.

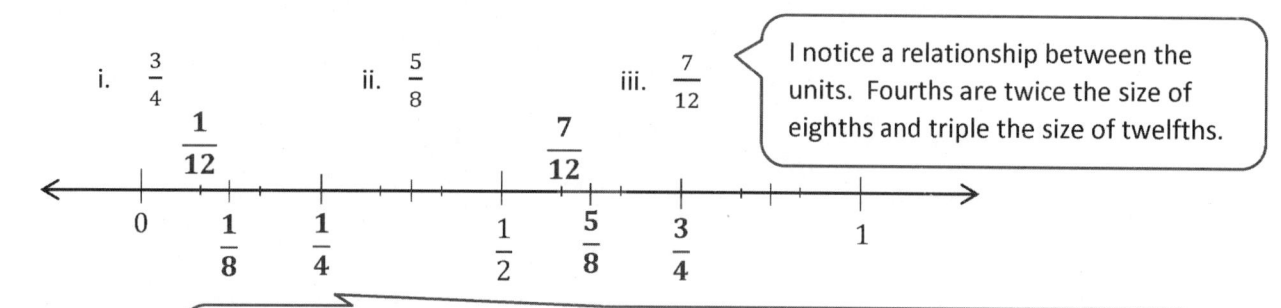

   i. $\frac{3}{4}$ ii. $\frac{5}{8}$ iii. $\frac{7}{12}$

   > I notice a relationship between the units. Fourths are twice the size of eighths and triple the size of twelfths.

   Number line marked with 0, $\frac{1}{8}$, $\frac{1}{12}$, $\frac{1}{4}$, $\frac{1}{2}$, $\frac{5}{8}$, $\frac{7}{12}$, $\frac{3}{4}$, 1.

   > I use benchmark fractions I know to plot twelfths. After marking fourths, I know that 1 fourth is the same as 3 twelfths, so I decompose each fourth into 3 units to make twelfths.

   b. Use the number line in part (a) to compare the fractions by writing >, <, or = on the lines.

   i. $\frac{3}{4}$ __>__ $\frac{1}{2}$ ii. $\frac{7}{12}$ __<__ $\frac{5}{8}$

   c. Explain how you plotted the points in Part (a).

   Sample Student Response:

   The number line was partitioned into halves. I doubled the units to make fourths. I plotted 3 fourths. I doubled the units again to make eighths. Knowing that 1 half and 4 eighths are equivalent fractions, I simply counted on 1 more eighth to plot 5 eighths. Lastly, I thought about twelfths and fourths. 1 fourth is the same as 3 twelfths. I marked twelfths by partitioning each fourth into 3 units. I plotted 7 twelfths.

2. Compare the fractions given below by writing < or > on the line.

   Give a brief explanation for each answer referring to the benchmarks of 0, $\frac{1}{2}$, and/or 1.

   $\frac{5}{8}$ __>__ $\frac{6}{10}$

   Possible student response:

   If I think about eighths, I know that 1 half is equal to 4 eighths. Therefore, 5 eighths is 1 eighth greater than 1 half.

   I also know that 5 tenths is equal to 1 half. 6 tenths is 1 tenth greater than 1 half. Comparing the size of the units, I know that 1 eighth is more than 1 tenth. So, 5 eighths is greater than 6 tenths.

   Lesson 11: Reason using benchmarks to compare two fractions on the number line.

   129

Name _____   Date _____

1. a. Plot the following points on the number line without measuring.

   i. $\frac{2}{3}$ ii. $\frac{1}{6}$ iii. $\frac{4}{10}$

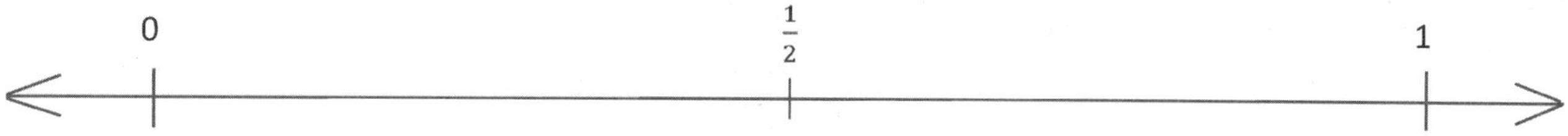

   ⟵—|———————————|———————————|——⟶
   0                $\frac{1}{2}$ 1

   b. Use the number line in Part (a) to compare the fractions by writing >, <, or = on the lines.

   i. $\frac{2}{3}$ _____ $\frac{1}{2}$ ii. $\frac{4}{10}$ _____ $\frac{1}{6}$

2. a. Plot the following points on the number line without measuring.

   i. $\frac{5}{12}$ ii. $\frac{3}{4}$ iii. $\frac{2}{6}$

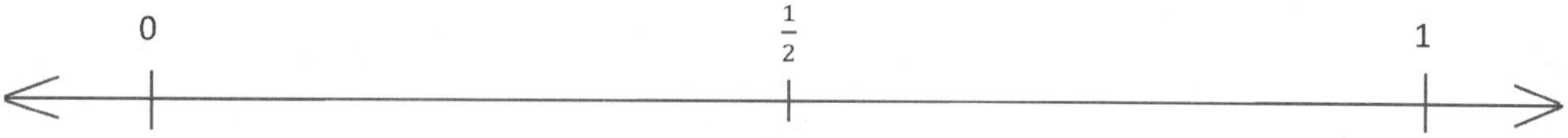

   ⟵—|———————————|———————————|——⟶
   0                $\frac{1}{2}$ 1

   b. Select two fractions from Part (a), and use the given number line to compare them by writing >, <, or =.

   c. Explain how you plotted the points in Part (a).

Lesson 11: Reason using benchmarks to compare two fractions on the number line.

3. Compare the fractions given below by writing > or < on the lines.
   Give a brief explanation for each answer referring to the benchmark of 0, $\frac{1}{2}$, and 1.

   a. $\frac{1}{2}$ _____ $\frac{1}{4}$

   b. $\frac{6}{8}$ _____ $\frac{1}{2}$

   c. $\frac{3}{4}$ _____ $\frac{3}{5}$

   d. $\frac{4}{6}$ _____ $\frac{9}{12}$

   e. $\frac{2}{3}$ _____ $\frac{1}{4}$

   f. $\frac{4}{5}$ _____ $\frac{8}{12}$

   g. $\frac{1}{3}$ _____ $\frac{3}{6}$

   h. $\frac{7}{8}$ _____ $\frac{3}{5}$

   i. $\frac{51}{100}$ _____ $\frac{5}{10}$

   j. $\frac{8}{14}$ _____ $\frac{49}{100}$

A STORY OF UNITS – TEKS EDITION

Lesson 12 Homework Helper   4•5

1. Place the following fractions on the number line given.

   a. $\dfrac{7}{4}$ b. $\dfrac{3}{2}$ c. $\dfrac{11}{8}$

   > $\dfrac{8}{4}$ is equal to 2. Therefore, $\dfrac{7}{4}$ is 1 fourth less than 2.

   > I can draw a number bond, breaking $\dfrac{11}{8}$ into $\dfrac{8}{8}$ and $\dfrac{3}{8}$.

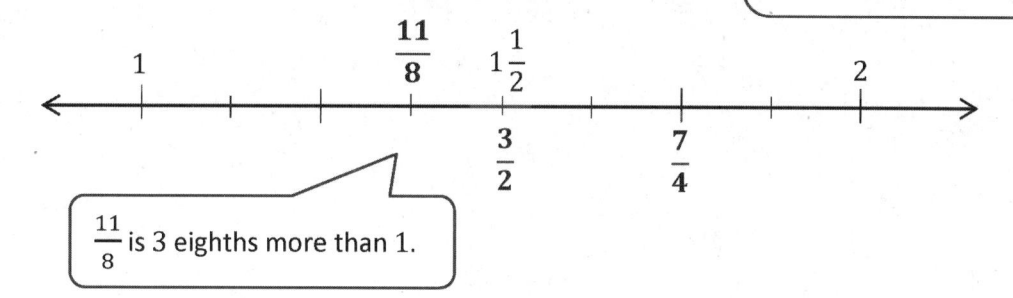

   Number line showing: 1, $\dfrac{11}{8}$, $1\dfrac{1}{2}$ (which is $\dfrac{3}{2}$), $\dfrac{7}{4}$, 2

   > $\dfrac{11}{8}$ is 3 eighths more than 1.

2. Use the number line in Problem 1 to compare the fractions by writing <, >, or = on the lines.

   a. $1\dfrac{3}{4}$ __>__ $1\dfrac{1}{2}$ b. $1\dfrac{3}{8}$ __<__ $1\dfrac{3}{4}$

   > Using the benchmark $\dfrac{1}{2}$, I compare the fractions. $1\dfrac{3}{8}$ is less than 1 and 1 half, while $1\dfrac{3}{4}$ is more than 1 and 1 half.

3. Use the number line in Problem 1 to explain the reasoning you used when determining whether $\dfrac{11}{8}$ or $\dfrac{7}{4}$ was greater.

   Sample Student Response:

   After I plotted $\dfrac{11}{8}$ and $\dfrac{7}{4}$, I noticed that $\dfrac{7}{4}$ was greater than $1\dfrac{1}{2}$, whereas $\dfrac{11}{8}$ is less than $1\dfrac{1}{2}$.

Lesson 12: Reason using benchmarks to compare two fractions on the number line.

4. Compare the fractions given below by writing < or > on the lines. Give a brief explanation for each answer referring to benchmarks.

a. $\frac{5}{4}$ __>__ $\frac{9}{10}$

$\frac{5}{4}$ is greater than 1.

$\frac{9}{10}$ is less than 1.

b. $\frac{7}{12}$ __<__ $\frac{7}{6}$ — I use two different benchmarks to compare these fractions.

$\frac{7}{12}$ is one twelfth greater than $\frac{1}{2}$.

$\frac{7}{6}$ is one sixth greater than 1.

A STORY OF UNITS – TEKS EDITION Lesson 12 Homework 4•5

Name _____ Date _____

1. Place the following fractions on the number line given.

   a. $\frac{3}{2}$ b. $\frac{9}{5}$ c. $\frac{14}{10}$

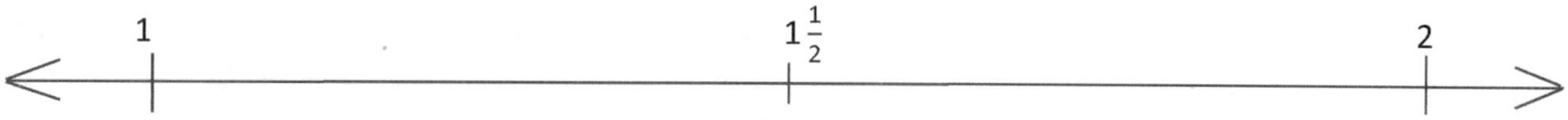

   ⟵——|————————————|————————————|——⟶
       1                         $1\frac{1}{2}$ 2

2. Use the number line in Problem 1 to compare the fractions by writing >, <, or = on the lines.

   a. $1\frac{1}{6}$ _____ $1\frac{4}{12}$ b. $1\frac{1}{2}$ _____ $1\frac{4}{5}$

3. Place the following fractions on the number line given.

   a. $\frac{12}{9}$ b. $\frac{6}{5}$ c. $\frac{18}{15}$

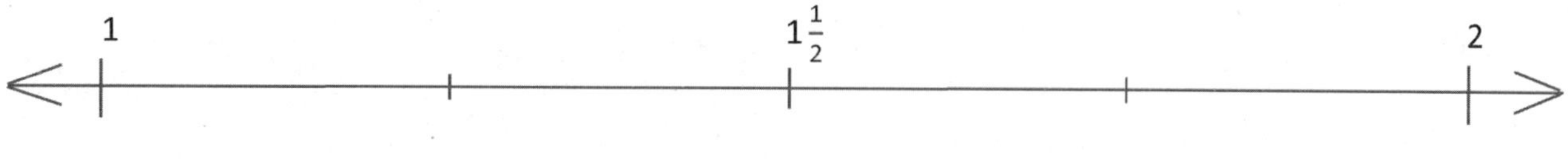

   ⟵—|————————|————————|————————|—⟶
      1                    $1\frac{1}{2}$ 2

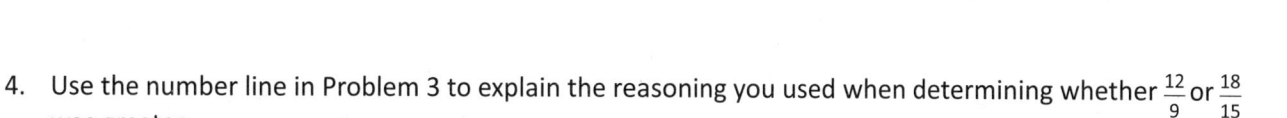

4. Use the number line in Problem 3 to explain the reasoning you used when determining whether $\frac{12}{9}$ or $\frac{18}{15}$ was greater.

Lesson 12: Reason using benchmarks to compare two fractions on the number line.

5. Compare the fractions given below by writing > or < on the lines. Give a brief explanation for each answer referring to benchmarks.

a. $\frac{2}{5}$ _____ $\frac{6}{8}$

b. $\frac{6}{10}$ _____ $\frac{5}{6}$

c. $\frac{6}{4}$ _____ $\frac{7}{8}$

d. $\frac{1}{4}$ _____ $\frac{8}{12}$

e. $\frac{14}{12}$ _____ $\frac{11}{6}$

f. $\frac{8}{9}$ _____ $\frac{3}{2}$

g. $\frac{7}{8}$ _____ $\frac{11}{10}$

h. $\frac{3}{4}$ _____ $\frac{4}{3}$

i. $\frac{3}{8}$ _____ $\frac{3}{2}$

j. $\frac{9}{6}$ _____ $\frac{16}{12}$

A STORY OF UNITS – TEKS EDITION Lesson 13 Homework Helper 4•5

1. Compare the pairs of fractions by reasoning about the size of the units. Use >, <, or =.

   a. 1 fourth __>__ 1 eighth   b. 2 thirds __>__ 2 fifths

   > I envision a strip diagram. 1 fourth is double the size of 1 eighth.

   > When I'm comparing the same number of units, I consider the size of the fractional unit. Thirds are bigger than fifths.

2. Compare by reasoning about the following pair of fractions with related numerators. Use >, <, or =. Explain your thinking using words, pictures, or numbers.

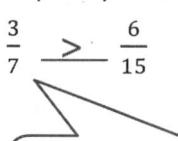

   $\frac{3}{7}$ __>__ $\frac{6}{15}$

   > To compare, I can make the numerators the same.

   3 sevenths are equal to 6 fourteenths. Fourteenths are greater than fifteenths. So, 3 sevenths are greater than 6 fifteenths.

3. Draw two strip diagrams to model and compare $1\frac{3}{4}$ and $1\frac{8}{12}$.

   $1\frac{3}{4}$ __>__ $1\frac{8}{12}$

   > The model shows that $\frac{9}{12}$ is equal to $\frac{3}{4}$. So, $\frac{8}{12}$ is less.

   > I'm careful to make each strip diagram the same size.

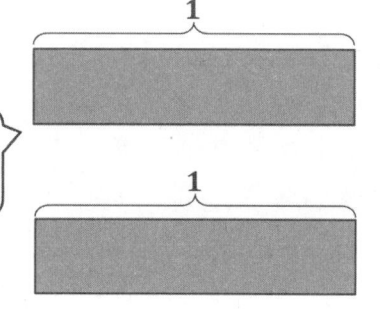

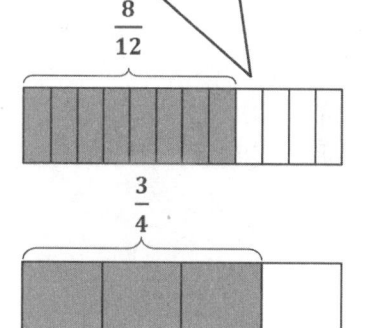

4. Draw one number line to model the pair of fractions with related denominators. Use >, <, or = to compare.

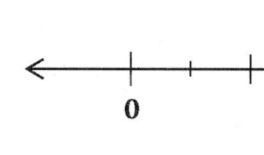

   $\frac{3}{12}$ __<__ $\frac{2}{6}$

Lesson 13: Find common units or number of units to compare two fractions.

Name _____ Date _____

1. Compare the pairs of fractions by reasoning about the size of the units. Use >, <, or =.

   a. 1 third _____ 1 sixth

   b. 2 halves _____ 2 thirds

   c. 2 fourths _____ 2 sixths

   d. 5 eighths _____ 5 tenths

2. Compare by reasoning about the following pairs of fractions with the same or related numerators. Use >, <, or =. Explain your thinking using words, pictures, or numbers. Problem 2(b) has been done for you.

   a. $\dfrac{3}{6}$ _____ $\dfrac{3}{7}$

   b. $\dfrac{2}{5} < \dfrac{4}{9}$

   because $\dfrac{2}{5} = \dfrac{4}{10}$

   4 tenths is less than 4 ninths because tenths are smaller than ninths.

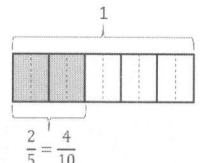

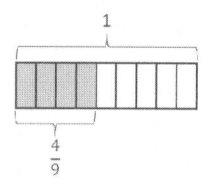

   c. $\dfrac{3}{11}$ _____ $\dfrac{3}{13}$

   d. $\dfrac{5}{7}$ _____ $\dfrac{10}{13}$

Lesson 13: Find common units or number of units to compare two fractions.

3. Draw two strip diagrams to model each pair of the following fractions with related denominators. Use >, <, or = to compare.

   a. $\frac{3}{4}$ _____ $\frac{7}{12}$

   b. $\frac{2}{4}$ _____ $\frac{1}{8}$

   c. $1\frac{4}{10}$ _____ $1\frac{3}{5}$

4. Draw one number line to model each pair of fractions with related denominators. Use >, <, or = to compare.

   a. $\dfrac{3}{4}$ _____ $\dfrac{5}{8}$

   b. $\dfrac{11}{12}$ _____ $\dfrac{3}{4}$

   c. $\dfrac{4}{5}$ _____ $\dfrac{7}{10}$

   d. $\dfrac{8}{9}$ _____ $\dfrac{2}{3}$

5. Compare each pair of fractions using >, <, or =. Draw a model if you choose to.

   a. $\dfrac{1}{7}$ _____ $\dfrac{2}{7}$

   b. $\dfrac{5}{7}$ _____ $\dfrac{11}{14}$

   c. $\dfrac{7}{10}$ _____ $\dfrac{3}{5}$

   d. $\dfrac{2}{3}$ _____ $\dfrac{9}{15}$

   e. $\dfrac{3}{4}$ _____ $\dfrac{9}{12}$

   f. $\dfrac{5}{3}$ _____ $\dfrac{5}{2}$

Lesson 13: Find common units or number of units to compare two fractions.

6. Simon claims $\frac{4}{9}$ is greater than $\frac{1}{3}$. Ted thinks $\frac{4}{9}$ is less than $\frac{1}{3}$. Who is correct? Support your answer with a picture.

A STORY OF UNITS – TEKS EDITION

Lesson 14 Homework Helper 4•5

1. Draw an area model for the pair of fractions, and use it to compare the two fractions by writing <, >, or = on the line.

   $\dfrac{4}{5}$ < $\dfrac{6}{7}$

   $\dfrac{28}{35}$ < $\dfrac{30}{35}$

   $\dfrac{4 \times 7}{5 \times 7} = \dfrac{28}{35}$

   $\dfrac{6 \times 5}{7 \times 5} = \dfrac{30}{35}$

   > I use two area models that are exactly the same size to find like units. After partitioning, I have 35 units in each model. Now I can compare!

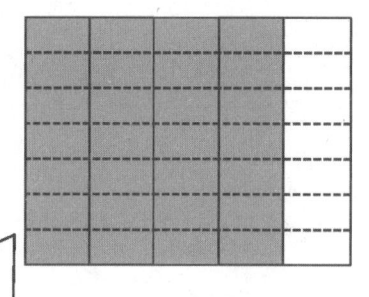

   > I represent fifths with vertical lines and then partition fifths by drawing horizontal lines.

   > I represent sevenths with horizontal lines and then partition sevenths by drawing vertical lines.

2. Rename the fractions below using multiplication, and then compare by writing <, >, or =.

   $\dfrac{5}{8}$ < $\dfrac{9}{12}$ $\dfrac{5 \times 12}{8 \times 12} = \dfrac{60}{96}$ $\dfrac{9 \times 8}{12 \times 8} = \dfrac{72}{96}$

   $\dfrac{60}{96}$ < $\dfrac{72}{96}$

   > Whew! That would have been a lot of units to draw in an area model!

   > Using multiplication to make common units is quick and precise. It is best to compare fractions when the units are the same.

Lesson 14: Find common units or number of units to compare two fractions.

3. Use any method to compare the fractions below. Record your answer using <, >, or =.

$\frac{5}{3}$ $<$ $\frac{9}{5}$

$\frac{3}{3}$ $=$ $\frac{5}{5}$

$\frac{2}{3}$ $<$ $\frac{4}{5}$

> I use benchmarks to compare. $\frac{4}{5}$ is closer to 1 than $\frac{2}{3}$ because fifths are smaller than thirds.

> I use number bonds to decompose fractions greater than 1. This lets me focus on the fractional parts, $\frac{2}{3}$ and $\frac{4}{5}$, to compare since $\frac{3}{3}$ and $\frac{5}{5}$ are equivalent.

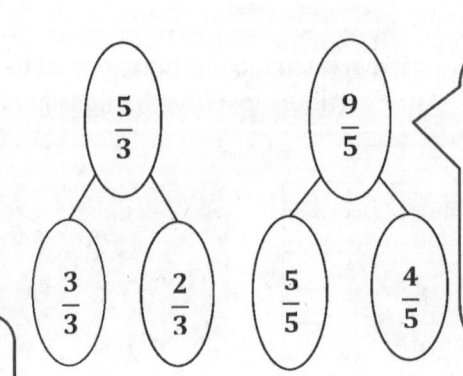

Lesson 14: Find common units or number of units to compare two fractions.

Name _____ Date _____

1. Draw an area model for each pair of fractions, and use it to compare the two fractions by writing >, <, or = on the line. The first two have been partially done for you. Each rectangle represents 1.

   a. $\dfrac{1}{2}$ __<__ $\dfrac{3}{5}$

   $\dfrac{1 \times 5}{2 \times 5} = \dfrac{5}{10}$ $\dfrac{3 \times 2}{5 \times 2} = \dfrac{6}{10}$

   $\dfrac{5}{10} < \dfrac{6}{10}$, so $\dfrac{1}{2} < \dfrac{3}{5}$

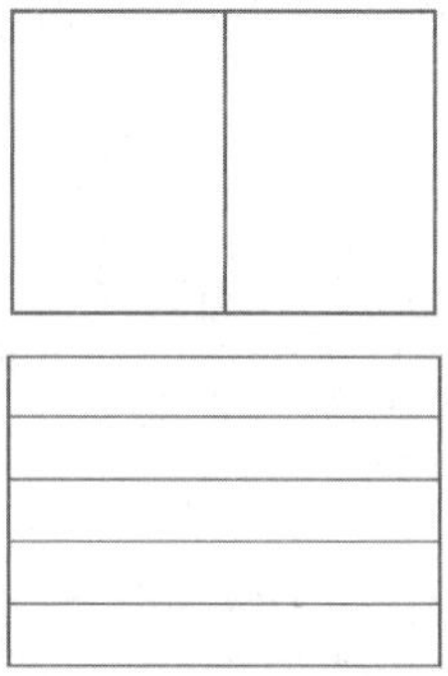

   b. $\dfrac{2}{3}$ _____ $\dfrac{3}{4}$

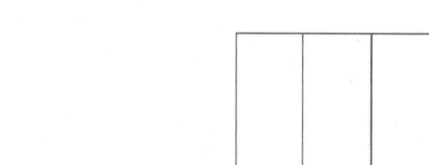

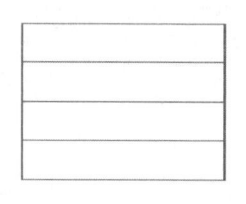

   c. $\dfrac{4}{6}$ _____ $\dfrac{5}{8}$

   d. $\dfrac{2}{7}$ _____ $\dfrac{3}{5}$

   e. $\dfrac{4}{6}$ _____ $\dfrac{6}{9}$

   f. $\dfrac{4}{5}$ _____ $\dfrac{5}{6}$

Lesson 14: Find common units or number of units to compare two fractions.

2. Rename the fractions, as needed, using multiplication in order to compare each pair of fractions by writing >, <, or =.

   a. $\dfrac{2}{3}$ _____ $\dfrac{2}{4}$

   b. $\dfrac{4}{7}$ _____ $\dfrac{1}{2}$

   c. $\dfrac{5}{4}$ _____ $\dfrac{9}{8}$

   d. $\dfrac{8}{12}$ _____ $\dfrac{5}{8}$

3. Use any method to compare the fractions. Record your answer using >, <, or =.

   a. $\dfrac{8}{9}$ _____ $\dfrac{2}{3}$

   b. $\dfrac{4}{7}$ _____ $\dfrac{4}{5}$

   c. $\dfrac{3}{2}$ _____ $\dfrac{9}{6}$

   d. $\dfrac{11}{7}$ _____ $\dfrac{5}{3}$

4. Explain which method you prefer using to compare fractions. Provide an example using words, pictures, or numbers.

A STORY OF UNITS – TEKS EDITION — Lesson 15 Homework Helper — 4•5

Solve.

1. 5 sixths − 3 sixths = __2 sixths__

> The units in both numbers are the same, so I can think "5 − 3 = 2," so 5 sixths − 3 sixths = 2 sixths.

> I can rewrite the number sentence using fractions.
> $$\frac{5}{6} - \frac{3}{6} = \frac{2}{6}$$

2. 1 sixth + 4 sixths = __5 sixths__

> If I know that 1 + 4 = 5, then 1 sixth + 4 sixths = 5 sixths.

Solve. Use a number bond to rename the sum or difference as a mixed number. Then, draw a number line to model your answer.

3. $\frac{12}{6} - \frac{5}{6} = \frac{7}{6} = 1\frac{1}{6}$

Number bond: $\frac{7}{6}$ → $\frac{6}{6}$ and $\frac{1}{6}$

> I can rename $\frac{7}{6}$ as a mixed number using a number bond to separate, or decompose, $\frac{7}{6}$ into a whole number and a fraction. $\frac{6}{6}$ is the whole, and the fractional part is $\frac{1}{6}$.

4. $\frac{5}{6} + \frac{5}{6} = \frac{10}{6} = 1\frac{4}{6}$

Number bond: $\frac{10}{6}$ → $\frac{6}{6}$ and $\frac{4}{6}$

> I decompose $\frac{10}{6}$ into 2 parts: $\frac{6}{6}$ and $\frac{4}{6}$. $\frac{6}{6}$ is the same as 1, so I rewrite $\frac{10}{6}$ as the mixed number $1\frac{4}{6}$.

> I can think of the number sentence in unit form: 5 sixths + 5 sixths = 10 sixths.

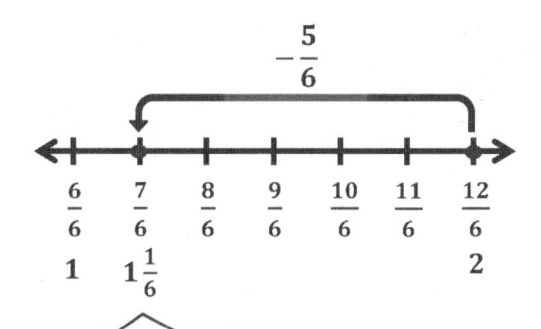

Number line (left): points from $\frac{6}{6}$ (1), $\frac{7}{6}$ ($1\frac{1}{6}$), $\frac{8}{6}$, $\frac{9}{6}$, $\frac{10}{6}$, $\frac{11}{6}$, $\frac{12}{6}$ (2), with arrow $-\frac{5}{6}$ from $\frac{12}{6}$ back to $\frac{7}{6}$.

Number line (right): points from $\frac{0}{6}$ (0) through $\frac{12}{6}$ (2), with arrow $+\frac{5}{6}$ from $\frac{5}{6}$ up to $\frac{10}{6}$ ($1\frac{4}{6}$).

> I plot a point at $\frac{12}{6}$ because that is the whole. Then, I count backward to subtract $\frac{5}{6}$.

> I draw a number line and plot a point at $\frac{5}{6}$. I count up $\frac{5}{6}$. The model verifies the sum is $1\frac{4}{6}$.

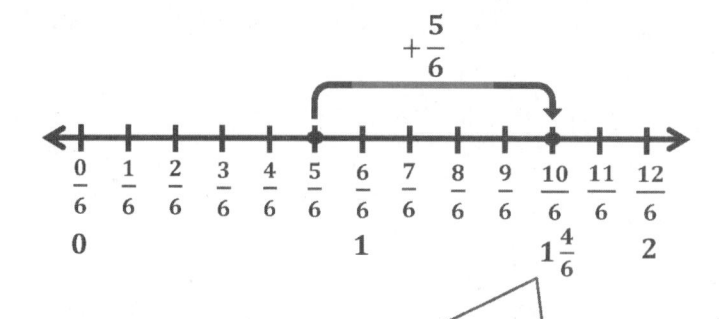

Lesson 15: Use visual models to add and subtract two fractions with the same units.

Name _____ Date _____

1. Solve.

   a. 3 sixths − 2 sixths = _____

   b. 5 tenths − 3 tenths = _____

   c. 3 fourths − 2 fourths = _____

   d. 5 thirds − 2 thirds = _____

2. Solve.

   a. $\frac{3}{5} - \frac{2}{5}$

   b. $\frac{7}{9} - \frac{3}{9}$

   c. $\frac{7}{12} - \frac{3}{12}$

   d. $\frac{6}{6} - \frac{4}{6}$

   e. $\frac{5}{3} - \frac{2}{3}$

   f. $\frac{7}{4} - \frac{5}{4}$

3. Solve. Use a number bond to decompose the difference. Record your final answer as a mixed number. Problem (a) has been completed for you.

   a. $\frac{12}{6} - \frac{3}{6} = \frac{9}{6} = 1\frac{3}{6}$

   $\frac{6}{6}$ $\frac{3}{6}$

   b. $\frac{17}{8} - \frac{6}{8}$

   c. $\frac{9}{5} - \frac{3}{5}$

   d. $\frac{11}{4} - \frac{6}{4}$

   e. $\frac{10}{7} - \frac{2}{7}$

   f. $\frac{21}{10} - \frac{9}{10}$

Lesson 15: Use visual models to add and subtract two fractions with the same units.

4. Solve. Write the sum in unit form.

   a. 4 fifths + 2 fifths = _____

   b. 5 eighths + 2 eighths = _____

5. Solve.

   a. $\frac{3}{11} + \frac{6}{11}$

   b. $\frac{3}{10} + \frac{6}{10}$

6. Solve. Use a number bond to decompose the sum. Record your final answer as a mixed number.

   a. $\frac{3}{4} + \frac{3}{4}$

   b. $\frac{8}{12} + \frac{6}{12}$

   c. $\frac{5}{8} + \frac{7}{8}$

   d. $\frac{8}{10} + \frac{5}{10}$

   e. $\frac{3}{5} + \frac{6}{5}$

   f. $\frac{4}{3} + \frac{2}{3}$

7. Solve. Use a number line to model your answer.

   a. $\frac{11}{9} - \frac{5}{9}$

   b. $\frac{13}{12} + \frac{4}{12}$

A STORY OF UNITS – TEKS EDITION

Lesson 16 Homework Helper 4•5

1. Use the three fractions $\frac{8}{8}, \frac{3}{8}$, and $\frac{5}{8}$ to write two addition and two subtraction number sentences.

   $\frac{3}{8} + \frac{5}{8} = \frac{8}{8}$ $\frac{8}{8} - \frac{5}{8} = \frac{3}{8}$

   $\frac{5}{8} + \frac{3}{8} = \frac{8}{8}$ $\frac{8}{8} - \frac{3}{8} = \frac{5}{8}$

   > This is like the relationship between 3, 5, and 8:
   > $3 + 5 = 8$ $8 - 5 = 3$
   > $5 + 3 = 8$ $8 - 3 = 5$
   > except these fractions have units of eighths.

2. Solve by subtracting and counting up. Model with a number line.

   $1 - \frac{3}{8}$

   $\frac{8}{8} - \frac{3}{8} = \frac{5}{8}$

   > I rename 1 as $\frac{8}{8}$. Now, I have like units, eighths, and I can subtract.

   > Or, I count up by thinking about how many eighths it takes to get from $\frac{3}{8}$ to $\frac{8}{8}$.
   >
   > $\frac{3}{8} + x = \frac{8}{8}$
   > $x = \frac{5}{8}$

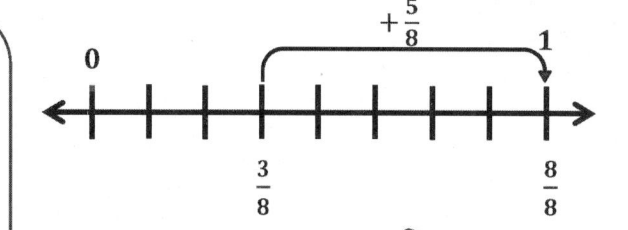

   > A number line shows how to count up from $\frac{3}{8}$ to $\frac{8}{8}$. I can also start at 1 and show the subtraction of $\frac{3}{8}$ on the number line.

3. Find the difference in two ways. Use a number bond to decompose the whole.

   $1\frac{5}{8} - \frac{7}{8}$

   $\frac{8}{8} + \frac{5}{8} = \frac{13}{8}$

   $\frac{13}{8} - \frac{7}{8} = \frac{6}{8}$

   $\frac{8}{8} - \frac{7}{8} = \frac{1}{8}$

   $\frac{1}{8} + \frac{5}{8} = \frac{6}{8}$

   > bond to rename $\frac{}{8}$ as – and –.

   > I rename – as a fraction greater than . I have like units, so I can subtract – from —.

   > Or, I can subtract – from –, or , first and then add the remaining part of the number bond, –.

Lesson 16: Use visual models to add and subtract two fractions with the same units, including subtracting from one whole.

153

A STORY OF UNITS – TEKS EDITION Lesson 16 Homework 4•5

Name _____ Date _____

1. Use the following three fractions to write two subtraction and two addition number sentences.

a. $\frac{5}{6}, \frac{4}{6}, \frac{9}{6}$	b. $\frac{5}{9}, \frac{13}{9}, \frac{8}{9}$

2. Solve. Model each subtraction problem with a number line, and solve by both counting up and subtracting.

   a. $1 - \frac{5}{8}$

   b. $1 - \frac{2}{5}$

   c. $1\frac{3}{6} - \frac{5}{6}$

   d. $1 - \frac{1}{4}$

   e. $1\frac{1}{3} - \frac{2}{3}$

   f. $1\frac{1}{5} - \frac{2}{5}$

Lesson 16: Use visual models to add and subtract two fractions with the same units, including subtracting from one whole.

3. Find the difference in two ways. Use number bonds to decompose the total. Part (a) has been completed for you.

a. $1\frac{2}{5} - \frac{4}{5}$

   Number bond: $\frac{5}{5}$ and $\frac{2}{5}$

   $\frac{5}{5} + \frac{2}{5} = \frac{7}{5}$

   $\frac{7}{5} - \frac{4}{5} = \boxed{\frac{3}{5}}$

   $\frac{5}{5} - \frac{4}{5} = \frac{1}{5}$

   $\frac{1}{5} + \frac{2}{5} = \boxed{\frac{3}{5}}$

b. $1\frac{3}{8} - \frac{7}{8}$

c. $1\frac{1}{4} - \frac{3}{4}$

d. $1\frac{2}{7} - \frac{5}{7}$

e. $1\frac{3}{10} - \frac{7}{10}$

A STORY OF UNITS – TEKS EDITION   Lesson 17 Homework Helper   4•5

Show two ways to solve each problem. Express the answer as a mixed number when possible. Use a number bond when it helps you.

1. $\frac{2}{5} + \frac{3}{5} + \frac{1}{5}$

$$\frac{2}{5} + \frac{3}{5} = \frac{5}{5} = 1$$

$$1 + \frac{1}{5} = 1\frac{1}{5}$$

> I can add $\frac{2}{5}$ and $\frac{3}{5}$ to make 1. Then, I can just add $\frac{1}{5}$ more to get $1\frac{1}{5}$.

$$\frac{2}{5} + \frac{3}{5} + \frac{1}{5} = \frac{6}{5} = 1\frac{1}{5}$$

Number bond: $\frac{6}{5}$ decomposes into $\frac{5}{5}$ and $\frac{1}{5}$.

> Since the units, or denominators, are the same for each addend, fifths, I can just add the number of units, or numerators.

> I can use a number bond to decompose $\frac{6}{5}$ into $\frac{5}{5}$ and $\frac{1}{5}$. Since $\frac{5}{5} = 1$, I can rewrite $\frac{6}{5}$ as $1\frac{1}{5}$.

2. $1 - \frac{3}{12} - \frac{4}{12}$

> I add $\frac{3}{12}$ and $\frac{4}{12}$ to get $\frac{7}{12}$. I need to subtract a total of $\frac{7}{12}$ from 1.

$$\frac{3}{12} + \frac{4}{12} = \frac{7}{12}$$

$$\frac{12}{12} - \frac{7}{12} = \frac{5}{12}$$

$$\frac{12}{12} - \frac{3}{12} = \frac{9}{12}$$

$$\frac{9}{12} - \frac{4}{12} = \frac{5}{12}$$

> I can rename 1 as $\frac{12}{12}$, and I can subtract $\frac{7}{12}$ from $\frac{12}{12}$.

> I rename 1 as $\frac{12}{12}$. Then, I subtract $\frac{3}{12}$, and finally I subtract $\frac{4}{12}$.

Lesson 17: Add and subtract more than two fractions.

Name _____ **Date** _____

1. Show one way to solve each problem. Express sums and differences as a mixed number when possible. Use number bonds when it helps you. Part (a) is partially completed.

a. $\frac{1}{3} + \frac{2}{3} + \frac{1}{3}$ $= \frac{3}{3} + \frac{1}{3} = 1 + \frac{1}{3}$ = _____	b. $\frac{5}{8} + \frac{5}{8} + \frac{3}{8}$	c. $\frac{4}{6} + \frac{6}{6} + \frac{1}{6}$
d. $1\frac{2}{12} - \frac{2}{12} - \frac{1}{12}$	e. $\frac{5}{7} + \frac{1}{7} + \frac{4}{7}$	f. $\frac{4}{10} + \frac{7}{10} + \frac{9}{10}$
g. $1 - \frac{3}{10} - \frac{1}{10}$	h. $1\frac{3}{5} - \frac{4}{5} - \frac{1}{5}$	i. $\frac{10}{15} + \frac{7}{15} + \frac{12}{15} + \frac{1}{15}$

Lesson 17: Add and subtract more than two fractions.

2. Bonnie used two different strategies to solve $\frac{5}{10} + \frac{4}{10} + \frac{3}{10}$.

Bonnie's First Strategy

$$\frac{5}{10} + \frac{4}{10} + \frac{3}{10} = \frac{9}{10} + \frac{3}{10} = \frac{10}{10} + \frac{2}{10} = 1\frac{2}{10}$$

with $\frac{3}{10}$ decomposed into $\frac{1}{10}$ and $\frac{2}{10}$

Bonnie's Second Strategy

$$\frac{5}{10} + \frac{4}{10} + \frac{3}{10} = \frac{12}{10} = 1 + \frac{2}{10} = 1\frac{2}{10}$$

with $\frac{12}{10}$ decomposed into $\frac{10}{10}$ and $\frac{2}{10}$

Which strategy do you like best? Why?

3. You gave one solution for each part of Problem 1. Now, for each problem indicated below, give a different solution method.

1(b) $\frac{5}{8} + \frac{5}{8} + \frac{3}{8}$

1(e) $\frac{5}{7} + \frac{1}{7} + \frac{4}{7}$

1(h) $1\frac{3}{5} - \frac{4}{5} - \frac{1}{5}$

A STORY OF UNITS – TEKS EDITION Lesson 18 Homework Helper 4•5

Use the RDW process to solve.

1. Noah drank $\frac{8}{10}$ liter of water on Monday and $\frac{6}{10}$ liter on Tuesday. How many liters of water did Noah drink in the 2 days?

w

| $\frac{8}{10}$ | $\frac{6}{10}$ |

$\frac{8}{10} + \frac{6}{10} = w$

> I add the parts in my strip diagram to find the total amount of water that Noah drank.

> I draw a strip diagram to model the problem. The parts in my strip diagram represent the water Noah drank on Monday and Tuesday. I use the variable w to represent the liters of water Noah drank on Monday and Tuesday.

$\frac{8}{10} + \frac{6}{10} = \frac{14}{10} = 1\frac{4}{10}$

$\frac{10}{10} \quad \frac{4}{10}$

> Since the addends have like units, I add the numerators to get $\frac{14}{10}$. I use a number bond to decompose $\frac{14}{10}$ into a whole number and a fraction. This helps me rename $\frac{14}{10}$ as a mixed number.

$w = 1\frac{4}{10}$

Noah drank $1\frac{4}{10}$ liters of water.

> I write a statement to answer the question. I also think about the reasonableness of my answer. The water drunk on each day is less than 1 liter, so I would expect to get a total less than 2 liters. My answer of $1\frac{4}{10}$ liters is a reasonable total amount.

Lesson 18: Solve word problems involving addition and subtraction of fractions.

161

2. Muneeb had 2 chapters to read for homework. By 9:00 p.m., he had read $1\frac{2}{7}$ chapters. What fraction of chapters is left for Muneeb to read?

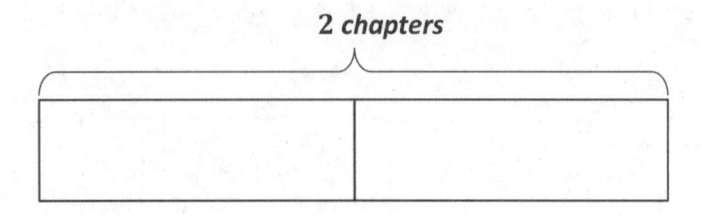

> I can draw a strip diagram with 2 equal parts to represent the 2 chapters of the book.

> To show $1\frac{2}{7}$ on my strip diagram, I partition one chapter into sevenths. I label the amount that Muneeb has read and the amount that is left, x.

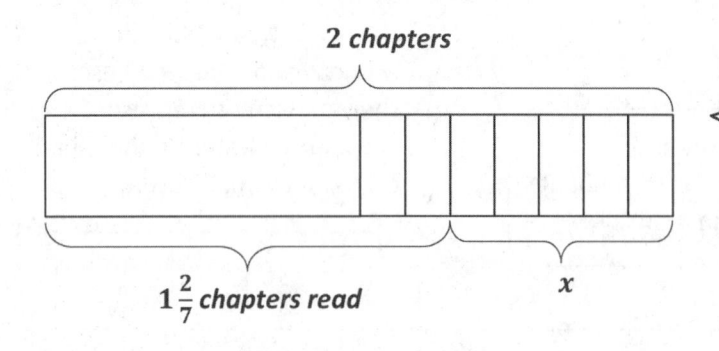

$2 - 1\frac{2}{7} = x$

> The unknown in my strip diagram is one of the parts, so I subtract the known part, $1\frac{2}{7}$, from the whole, 2.

$2 - 1\frac{2}{7} = \frac{5}{7}$

> I use a number bond to show how to decompose one of the chapters into sevenths. My strip diagram shows that there is $\frac{5}{7}$ of a chapter left. My equation shows that, too!

$1 \quad \frac{7}{7}$

$x = \frac{5}{7}$

Muneeb has $\frac{5}{7}$ chapter left to read.

> Muneeb started with 2 chapters to read. He read 1 chapter and a little more, so he should have less than 1 chapter left. My answer of $\frac{5}{7}$ chapter is a reasonable amount left because it's less than 1 chapter.

Name _____ **Date** _____

Use the RDW process to solve.

1. Isla walked $\frac{3}{4}$ mile each way to and from school on Wednesday. How many miles did Isla walk that day?

2. Zach spent $\frac{2}{3}$ hour reading on Friday and $1\frac{1}{3}$ hours reading on Saturday. How much more time did he read on Saturday than on Friday?

3. Mrs. Cashmore bought a large melon. She cut a piece that weighed $1\frac{1}{8}$ pounds and gave it to her neighbor. The remaining piece of melon weighed $\frac{6}{8}$ pound. How much did the whole melon weigh?

4. Ally's little sister wanted to help her make some oatmeal cookies. First, she put $\frac{5}{8}$ cup of oatmeal in the bowl. Next, she added another $\frac{5}{8}$ cup of oatmeal. Finally, she added another $\frac{5}{8}$ cup of oatmeal. How much oatmeal did she put in the bowl?

5. Mark baked 2 pans of brownies. His family ate $1\frac{5}{6}$ pans. What fraction of a pan of brownies was left?

6. Joanie wrote a letter that was $1\frac{1}{4}$ pages long. Katie wrote a letter that was $\frac{3}{4}$ page shorter than Joanie's letter. How long was Katie's letter?

A STORY OF UNITS – TEKS EDITION   Lesson 19 Homework Helper   4•5

1. Draw a strip diagram to match the number sentence. Then, complete the number sentence.

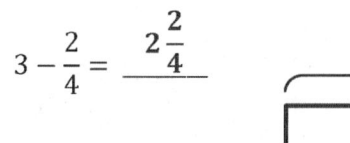

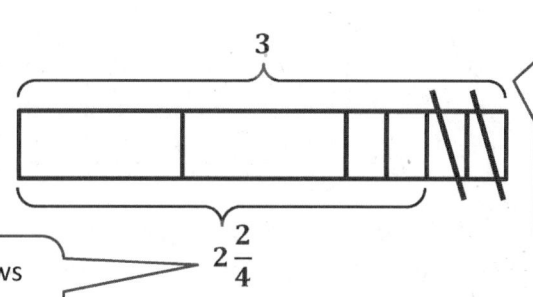

$3 - \frac{2}{4} = \underline{2\frac{2}{4}}$

> I draw a strip diagram with 3 equal units, with 1 unit decomposed into fourths. To show the subtraction, I cross off $\frac{2}{4}$.

> The strip diagram shows the difference is $2\frac{2}{4}$.

2. Use $\frac{5}{6}$, 3, and $2\frac{1}{6}$ to write two subtraction and two addition number sentences.

$\frac{5}{6} + 2\frac{1}{6} = 3$ $3 - \frac{5}{6} = 2\frac{1}{6}$

$2\frac{1}{6} + \frac{5}{6} = 3$ $3 - 2\frac{1}{6} = \frac{5}{6}$

> I can also represent the relationship between these 3 numbers with a number bond.

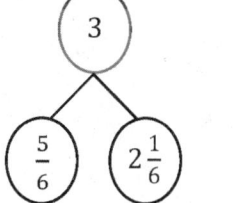

3. Solve using a number bond. Draw a number line to represent the number sentence.

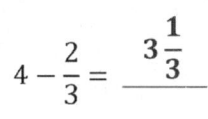

$4 - \frac{2}{3} = \underline{3\frac{1}{3}}$

$4 - \frac{2}{3} = 3\frac{1}{3}$

> I use a number bond to decompose 4 into 3 and $\frac{3}{3}$. Then, I subtract $\frac{2}{3}$ from $\frac{3}{3}$.

> I draw a number line with the endpoints 3 and 4 because I am starting at 4 and subtracting a number less than 1.

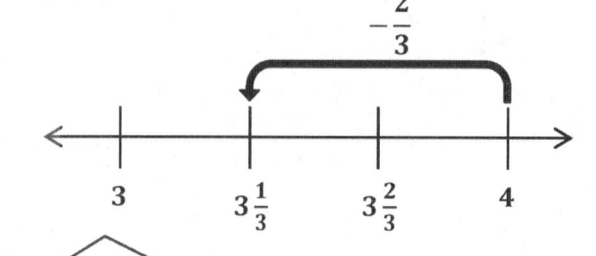

Lesson 19: Add a fraction less than 1 to, or subtract a fraction less than 1 from, a whole number using decomposition and visual models.

4. Complete the subtraction sentence using a number bond.

$6 - \frac{6}{8} = 5\frac{2}{8}$

Number bond: 6 decomposes into 5 and $\frac{8}{8}$

$\frac{8}{8} - \frac{6}{8} = \frac{2}{8}$

$5 + \frac{2}{8} = 5\frac{2}{8}$

> I subtract $\frac{6}{8}$ from $\frac{8}{8}$ to get $\frac{2}{8}$. I add $\frac{2}{8}$ back to 5.

A STORY OF UNITS – TEKS EDITION Lesson 19 Homework 4•5

Name _____ Date _____

1. Draw a strip diagram to match each number sentence. Then, complete the number sentence.

   a. $2 + \frac{1}{4} =$ _____

   b. $3 + \frac{2}{3} =$ _____

   c. $2 - \frac{1}{5} =$ _____

   d. $3 - \frac{3}{4} =$ _____

2. Use the following three numbers to write two subtraction and two addition number sentences.

   a. $4, 4\frac{5}{8}, \frac{5}{8}$

   b. $\frac{2}{7}, 5\frac{5}{7}, 6$

3. Solve using a number bond. Draw a number line to represent each number sentence. The first one has been done for you.

   a. $4 - \frac{1}{3} = 3\frac{2}{3}$

   b. $8 - \frac{5}{6} =$ _____

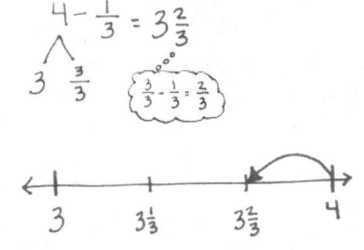

Lesson 19: Add a fraction less than 1 to, or subtract a fraction less than 1 from, a whole number using decomposition and visual models.

c. $7 - \frac{4}{5} =$ _____ d. $3 - \frac{3}{10} =$ _____

4. Complete the subtraction sentences using number bonds.

   a. $6 - \frac{1}{4} =$ _____ b. $7 - \frac{2}{10} =$ _____

   c. $5 - \frac{5}{6} =$ _____ d. $6 - \frac{6}{8} =$ _____

   e. $3 - \frac{7}{8} =$ _____ f. $26 - \frac{7}{10} =$ _____

A STORY OF UNITS – TEKS EDITION   Lesson 20 Homework Helper   4•5

1. Rename $\frac{10}{3}$ as a mixed number by decomposing it into two parts. Model the decomposition with a number line and a number bond.

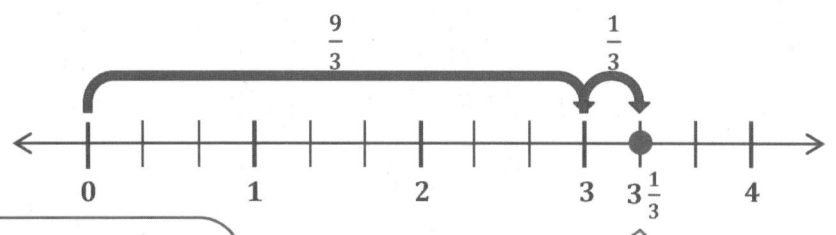

$$\frac{10}{3} = \frac{9}{3} + \frac{1}{3} = 3 + \frac{1}{3} = 3\frac{1}{3}$$

Number bond: $\frac{10}{3}$ decomposes into $\frac{9}{3}$ and $\frac{1}{3}$.

Number line shows jumps of $\frac{9}{3}$ from 0 to 3, then $\frac{1}{3}$ from 3 to $3\frac{1}{3}$.

> I choose the 2 parts $\frac{9}{3}$ and $\frac{1}{3}$ for the number bond because $\frac{9}{3}$ is 3 groups of $\frac{3}{3}$, or 3. Then, I add the other part of my number bond, $\frac{1}{3}$, to get the mixed number $3\frac{1}{3}$.

> The number line shows that decomposing $\frac{10}{3}$ as $\frac{9}{3}$ and $\frac{1}{3}$ is the same as $3\frac{1}{3}$.

2. Convert $\frac{22}{7}$ to a mixed number.

$$\frac{22}{7} = \frac{21}{7} + \frac{1}{7} = 3 + \frac{1}{7} = 3\frac{1}{7}$$

> I can make 3 groups of $\frac{7}{7}$, which equals $\frac{21}{7}$.
> I can add 1 more seventh to equal $\frac{22}{7}$.

Lesson 20: Decompose and compose fractions greater than 1 to express them in various forms.

Name _____   Date _____

1. Rename each fraction as a mixed number by decomposing it into two parts as shown below. Model the decomposition with a number line and a number bond.

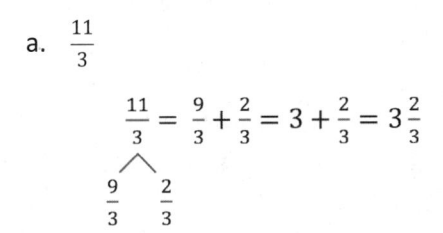

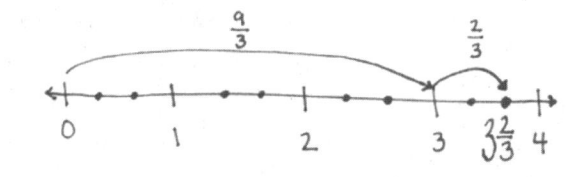

    a. $\dfrac{11}{3}$

    $\dfrac{11}{3} = \dfrac{9}{3} + \dfrac{2}{3} = 3 + \dfrac{2}{3} = 3\dfrac{2}{3}$

    b. $\dfrac{13}{4}$

    c. $\dfrac{16}{5}$

    d. $\dfrac{15}{2}$

    e. $\dfrac{17}{3}$

Lesson 20: Decompose and compose fractions greater than 1 to express them in various forms.

2. Convert each fraction to a mixed number.

a. $\frac{14}{3} =$	b. $\frac{17}{4} =$	c. $\frac{27}{5} =$
d. $\frac{28}{6} =$	e. $\frac{23}{7} =$	f. $\frac{37}{8} =$
g. $\frac{51}{9} =$	h. $\frac{74}{10} =$	i. $\frac{45}{12} =$

1. Convert the mixed number $2\frac{2}{4}$ to a fraction greater than 1. Draw a number line to model your work.

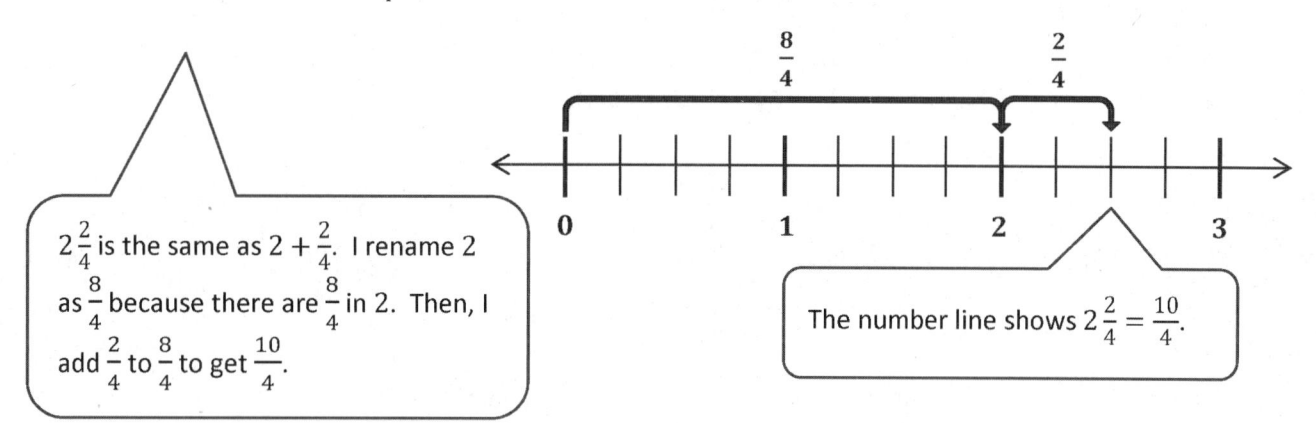

$2\frac{2}{4}$ is the same as $2 + \frac{2}{4}$. I rename 2 as $\frac{8}{4}$ because there are $\frac{8}{4}$ in 2. Then, I add $\frac{2}{4}$ to $\frac{8}{4}$ to get $\frac{10}{4}$.

The number line shows $2\frac{2}{4} = \frac{10}{4}$.

2. Convert the mixed number $6\frac{1}{3}$ to a fraction greater than 1.

$$6\frac{1}{3} = \frac{18}{3} + \frac{1}{3} = \frac{19}{3}$$

I use mental math. There are 6 ones and 1 third in the number $6\frac{1}{3}$. I know that there are 18 thirds in 6 ones. 18 thirds plus 1 more third is 19 thirds.

Lesson 21: Decompose and compose fractions greater than 1 to express them in various forms.

Name _____ Date _____

1. Convert each mixed number to a fraction greater than 1. Draw a number line to model your work.

   a. $3\frac{1}{4}$

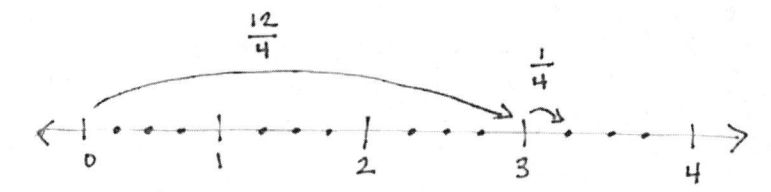

   $3\frac{1}{4} = 3 + \frac{1}{4} = \frac{12}{4} + \frac{1}{4} = \frac{13}{4}$

   b. $4\frac{2}{5}$

   c. $5\frac{3}{8}$

   d. $3\frac{7}{10}$

   e. $6\frac{2}{9}$

Lesson 21: Decompose and compose fractions greater than 1 to express them in various forms.

2. Convert each mixed number to a fraction greater than 1.

a. $2\frac{1}{3}$	b. $2\frac{3}{4}$	c. $3\frac{2}{5}$
d. $3\frac{1}{6}$	e. $4\frac{5}{12}$	f. $4\frac{2}{5}$
g. $4\frac{1}{10}$	h. $5\frac{1}{5}$	i. $5\frac{5}{6}$
j. $6\frac{1}{4}$	k. $7\frac{1}{2}$	l. $7\frac{11}{12}$

A STORY OF UNITS – TEKS EDITION
Lesson 22 Homework Helper 4•5

1.
   a. Plot the following points on the number line without measuring.

   i. $6\frac{7}{8}$ ii. $\frac{36}{5} = 7\frac{1}{5}$ iii. $\frac{19}{3} = 6\frac{1}{3}$

   > To plot the numbers on the number line, I rewrite $\frac{36}{5}$ and $\frac{19}{3}$ as mixed numbers.

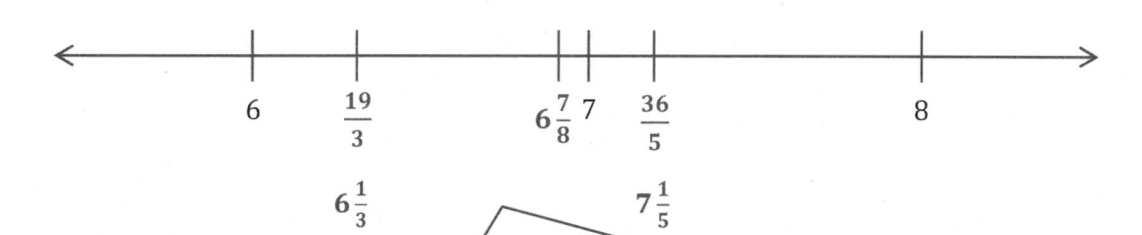

   Number line with points: 6, $\frac{19}{3}$ ($6\frac{1}{3}$), $6\frac{7}{8}$, 7, $\frac{36}{5}$ ($7\frac{1}{5}$), 8

   > I estimate to plot each number on the number line. I know that $6\frac{7}{8}$ is $\frac{1}{8}$ less than 7. I use this strategy to plot $6\frac{1}{3}$ and $7\frac{1}{5}$.

   b. Use the number line in Part 1(a) to compare the numbers by writing >, <, or =.

   i. $\frac{19}{3}$ __<__ $6\frac{7}{8}$ ii. $\frac{36}{5}$ __>__ $\frac{19}{3}$

   > I remember from Lessons 12 and 13 how I used the benchmarks of 0, $\frac{1}{2}$, and 1 to compare. $\frac{19}{3}$ is less than $6\frac{1}{2}$, and $6\frac{7}{8}$ is greater than $6\frac{1}{2}$. $\frac{36}{5}$ is greater than 7 and $\frac{19}{3}$ is less than 7.

Lesson 22: Compare fractions greater than 1 by reasoning using benchmark fractions.

177

2. Compare the fractions given below by writing >, <, or =. Give a brief explanation for each answer, referring to benchmark fractions.

a. $4\frac{4}{8}$ __>__ $4\frac{2}{5}$

$4\frac{4}{8}$ *is the same as* $4\frac{1}{2}$. $4\frac{2}{5}$ *is less than* $4\frac{1}{2}$, *so* $4\frac{4}{8}$ *is greater than* $4\frac{2}{5}$.

b. $\frac{43}{9}$ __<__ $\frac{35}{7}$

$\frac{35}{7}$ *is the same as* 5. $\frac{43}{9}$ *needs* 2 *more ninths to equal* 5. *That means that* $\frac{35}{7}$ *is greater than* $\frac{43}{9}$.

Name _____   Date _____

1. a. Plot the following points on the number line without measuring.

   i. $2\frac{1}{6}$ ii. $3\frac{3}{4}$ iii. $\frac{33}{9}$

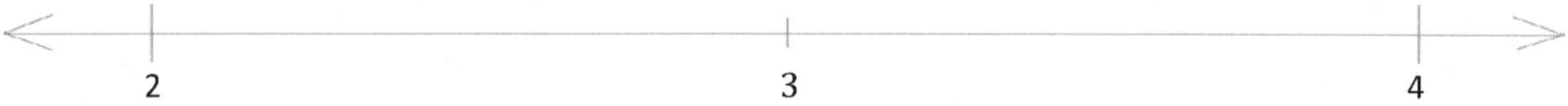

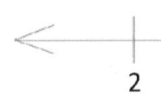

   <--+------------------+------------------+--->
      2   3   4

   b. Use the number line in Problem 1(a) to compare the fractions by writing >, <, or =.

   i. $\frac{33}{9}$ _____ $2\frac{1}{6}$ ii. $\frac{33}{9}$ _____ $3\frac{3}{4}$

2. a. Plot the following points on the number line without measuring.

   i. $\frac{65}{8}$ ii. $8\frac{5}{6}$ iii. $\frac{29}{4}$

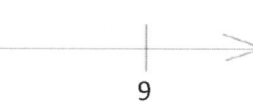

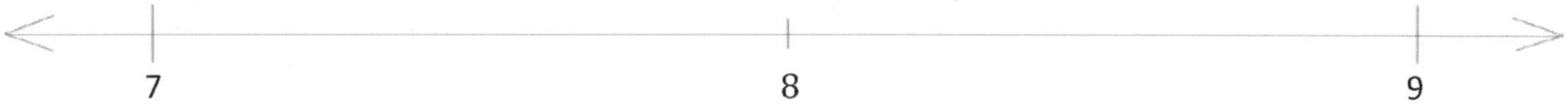

   <--+------------------+------------------+--->
      7   8   9

   b. Compare the following by writing >, <, or =.

   i. $8\frac{5}{6}$ _____ $\frac{65}{8}$ ii. $\frac{29}{4}$ _____ $\frac{65}{8}$

   c. Explain how you plotted the points in Problem 2(a).

Lesson 22: Compare fractions greater than 1 by reasoning using benchmark fractions.

3. Compare the fractions given below by writing >, <, or =. Give a brief explanation for each answer, referring to benchmark fractions.

a. $5\frac{1}{3}$ _____ $5\frac{3}{4}$

b. $\frac{12}{4}$ _____ $\frac{25}{8}$

c. $\frac{18}{6}$ _____ $\frac{17}{4}$

d. $5\frac{3}{5}$ _____ $5\frac{5}{10}$

e. $6\frac{3}{4}$ _____ $6\frac{3}{5}$

f. $\frac{33}{6}$ _____ $\frac{34}{7}$

g. $\frac{23}{10}$ _____ $\frac{20}{8}$

h. $\frac{27}{12}$ _____ $\frac{15}{6}$

i. $2\frac{49}{50}$ _____ $2\frac{99}{100}$

j. $6\frac{5}{9}$ _____ $6\frac{49}{100}$

A STORY OF UNITS – TEKS EDITION   Lesson 23 Homework Helper 4•5

1. Draw a strip diagram to model the comparison. Use >, <, or = to compare.

   $5\frac{7}{8}$ __>__ $\frac{23}{4}$

   $\frac{23}{4} = 5\frac{3}{4}$

   $\frac{20}{4}$ $\frac{3}{4}$

   $\frac{7}{8}$

   $\frac{3}{4} = \frac{6}{8}$

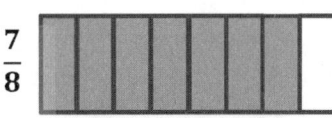

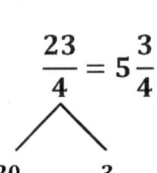

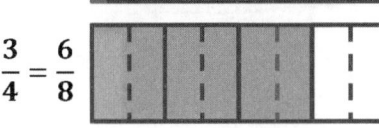

   > I can rename $\frac{23}{4}$ as a mixed number, $5\frac{3}{4}$.

   > Since both numbers have 5 ones, I draw strip diagrams to represent the fractional parts of each number. I decompose fourths to eighths. My strip diagrams show that $\frac{3}{4} = \frac{6}{8}$ and $\frac{7}{8} > \frac{6}{8}$.

2. Use an area model to make like units. Then, use >, <, or = to compare.

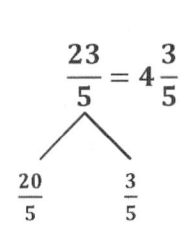

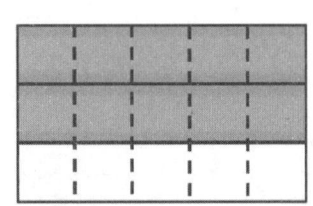

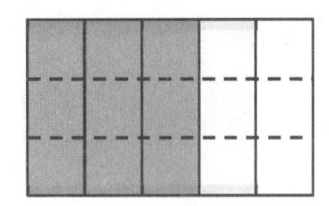

   $4\frac{2}{3}$ __>__ $\frac{23}{5}$

   $\frac{23}{5} = 4\frac{3}{5}$

   $\frac{20}{5}$ $\frac{3}{5}$

   $\frac{2}{3} = \frac{10}{15}$

   $\frac{3}{5} = \frac{9}{15}$

   > I draw area models to represent the fractional parts of each number. I make like units by drawing fifths vertically on the thirds and thirds horizontally on the fifths.

Lesson 23: Compare fractions greater than 1 by creating common numerators or denominators.

3. Compare each pair of fractions using >, <, or = using any strategy.

   a. $\dfrac{14}{6}$ __>__ $\dfrac{14}{9}$

   > Both fractions have the same numerator. Since sixths are bigger than ninths, $\dfrac{14}{6} > \dfrac{14}{9}$.

   b. $\dfrac{19}{4}$ __<__ $\dfrac{25}{5}$

   > $\dfrac{25}{5} = 5$, and $\dfrac{19}{4} < 5$ because is takes 20 fourths to equal 5.

   c. $6\dfrac{2}{6}$ __>__ $6\dfrac{4}{9}$

   $\dfrac{2 \times 3}{6 \times 3} = \dfrac{6}{18}$

   $\dfrac{4 \times 2}{9 \times 2} = \dfrac{8}{18}$

   $\dfrac{6}{18} < \dfrac{8}{18}$

   > I make like units, eighteenths, and compare.

Lesson 23: Compare fractions greater than 1 by creating common numerators or denominators.

Name _____ Date _____

1. Draw a strip diagram to model each comparison. Use >, <, or = to compare.

   a. $2\frac{3}{4}$ _____ $2\frac{7}{8}$

   b. $10\frac{2}{6}$ _____ $10\frac{1}{3}$

   c. $5\frac{3}{8}$ _____ $5\frac{1}{4}$

   d. $2\frac{5}{9}$ _____ $\frac{21}{3}$

2. Use an area model to make like units. Then, use >, <, or = to compare.

   a. $2\frac{4}{5}$ _____ $\frac{11}{4}$

   b. $2\frac{3}{5}$ _____ $2\frac{2}{3}$

Lesson 23: Compare fractions greater than 1 by creating common numerators or denominators.

3. Compare each pair of fractions using >, <, or = using any strategy.

a. $6\frac{1}{2}$ _____ $6\frac{3}{8}$

b. $7\frac{5}{6}$ _____ $7\frac{11}{12}$

c. $3\frac{6}{10}$ _____ $3\frac{2}{5}$

d. $2\frac{2}{5}$ _____ $2\frac{8}{15}$

e. $\frac{10}{3}$ _____ $\frac{10}{4}$

f. $\frac{12}{4}$ _____ $\frac{10}{3}$

g. $\frac{30}{9}$ _____ $4\frac{2}{12}$

h. $\frac{23}{4}$ _____ $5\frac{2}{3}$

i. $\frac{30}{8}$ _____ $3\frac{7}{12}$

j. $10\frac{3}{4}$ _____ $10\frac{4}{6}$

Lesson 23: Compare fractions greater than 1 by creating common numerators or denominators.

A STORY OF UNITS – TEKS EDITION   Lesson 24 Homework Helper   4•5

1. A group of students recorded the amount of time they spent doing homework in a week. The times are shown in the table. Make a dot plot to display the data.

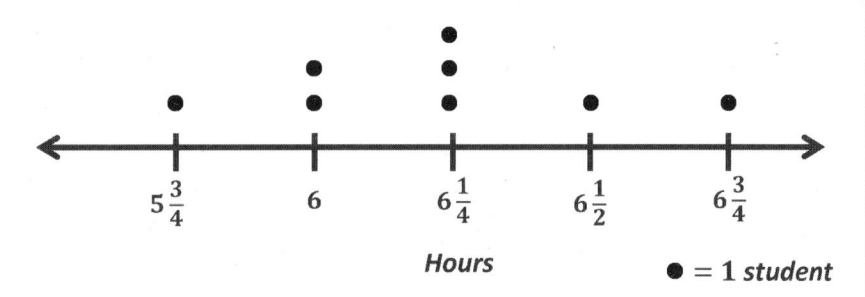

Student	Time Spent Doing Homework (in hours)
Rebecca	$6\frac{1}{4}$ ✓
Noah	6 ✓
Wilson	$5\frac{3}{4}$ ✓
Jenna	$6\frac{1}{4}$ ✓
Sam	$6\frac{1}{2}$ ✓
Angie	6 ✓
Matthew	$6\frac{1}{4}$ ✓
Jessica	$6\frac{3}{4}$ ✓

I can make a dot plot with an interval of fourths because that's the smallest unit in the table. My endpoints are $5\frac{3}{4}$ and $6\frac{3}{4}$ because those are the shortest and longest times spent doing homework. I can draw a dot above the correct time on the number line to represent the time each student spent doing homework.

Time Spent Doing Homework in One Week

Hours   ● = 1 student

2. Solve each problem.

   a. Who spent 1 hour longer doing homework than Wilson?

   $5\frac{3}{4} + 1 = 6\frac{3}{4}$

   I can add 1 hour to Wilson's time and look at the table to find the answer.

   Jessica spent 1 hour longer doing homework than Wilson.

   b. How many quarter hours did Jenna spend doing homework?

   $6\frac{1}{4} = \frac{24}{4} + \frac{1}{4} = \frac{25}{4}$

   Jenna spent 25 quarter hours doing her homework.

Lesson 24: Solve word problems with dot plots.

c. What is the difference, in hours, between the most frequent amount of time spent doing homework and the second most frequent amount of time spent doing homework?

$6\frac{1}{4} - 6 = \frac{1}{4}$

The difference is 1 fourth hour.

> The dots on the dot plot help me see the most frequent time, $6\frac{1}{4}$ hours, and the second most frequent time, 6 hours.

d. Compare the times of Matthew and Sam using >, <, or =.

$6\frac{1}{4} < 6\frac{1}{2}$

Matthew spent less time doing his homework than Sam.

e. How many students spent less than $6\frac{1}{2}$ hours doing their homework?

Six students spent less than $6\frac{1}{2}$ hours doing their homework.

> I can count the dots on the dot plot for $5\frac{3}{4}$ hours, 6 hours, and $6\frac{1}{4}$ hours.

f. How many students recorded the amount of time they spent doing their homework?

Eight students recorded the amount of time they spent doing their homework.

> I can count the dots on the dot plot, or I can count the students in the table.

g. Scott spent $\frac{30}{4}$ hours in one week doing his homework. Use >, <, or = to compare Scott's time to the time of the student who spent the most hours doing homework. Who spent more time doing homework?

$\frac{30}{4} = \frac{28}{4} + \frac{2}{4} = 7 + \frac{2}{4} = 7\frac{2}{4}$

$7\frac{2}{4} > 6\frac{3}{4}$

> I can rename Scott's time as a mixed number, and then I can compare (or I can rename Jessica's time as a fraction greater than 1). There are 7 ones in Scott's time and only 6 ones in Jessica's time.

Scott spent more time than Jessica doing homework.

Name _____ Date _____

1. A group of students measured the lengths of their shoes. The measurements are shown in the table. Make a dot plot to display the data.

Students	Length of shoe (in inches)
Collin	$8\frac{1}{2}$
Dickon	$7\frac{3}{4}$
Ben	$7\frac{1}{2}$
Martha	$7\frac{3}{4}$
Lilias	8
Susan	$8\frac{1}{2}$
Frances	$7\frac{3}{4}$
Mary	$8\frac{3}{4}$

2. Solve each problem.

   a. Who has a shoe length 1 inch longer than Dickon's?

   b. Who has a shoe length 1 inch shorter than Susan's?

Lesson 24: Solve word problems with dot plots.

c. How many quarter inches long is Martha's shoe length?

d. What is the difference, in inches, between Lilias's and Martha's shoe lengths?

e. Compare the shoe length of Ben and Frances using >, <, or =.

f. How many students had shoes that measured less than 8 inches?

g. How many students measured the length of their shoes?

h. Mr. Jones's shoe length was $\frac{25}{2}$ inches. Use >, <, or = to compare the length of Mr. Jones's shoe to the length of the longest student shoe length. Who had the longer shoe?

3. Using the information in the table and on the dot plot, write a question you could solve by using the dot plot. Solve.

A STORY OF UNITS – TEKS EDITION   Lesson 25 Homework Helper   4•5

1. Estimate each sum or difference to the nearest half or whole number by rounding. Explain your estimate using words or a number line.

   a. $4\frac{1}{9} + 2\frac{4}{5} \approx \underline{7}$

   $4\frac{1}{9}$ *is close to 4, and* $2\frac{4}{5}$ *is close to 3.* $4 + 3 = 7$

   $4\frac{1}{9}$ is 1 ninth more than 4. $2\frac{4}{5}$ is 1 fifth less than 3.

   b. $7\frac{5}{6} - 2\frac{1}{4} \approx \underline{6}$

   estimated difference $8 - 2 = 6$

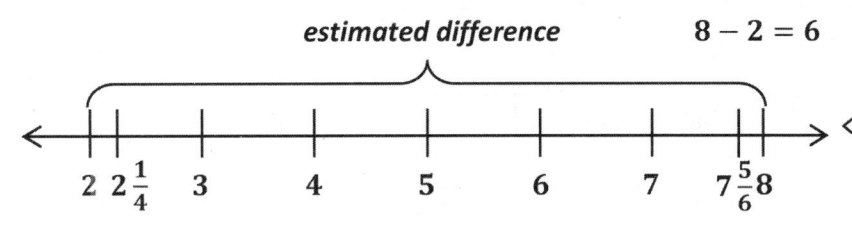

   ← | | | | | | | | | →
   2 $2\frac{1}{4}$ 3   4   5   6   7 $7\frac{5}{6}$ 8

   I draw a number line and plot the mixed numbers. It's easy to see on my number line that $7\frac{5}{6}$ is close to 8 and $2\frac{1}{4}$ is close to 2.

   My number line makes it easy to see that the estimated difference is larger than the actual difference because I rounded one number up and the other number down.

   c. $5\frac{4}{10} + 3\frac{1}{8} \approx \underline{8\frac{1}{2}}$

   $5\frac{4}{10}$ *is close to* $5\frac{1}{2}$*, and* $3\frac{1}{8}$ *is close to 3.* $5\frac{1}{2} + 3 = 8\frac{1}{2}$

   d. $\frac{15}{7} + \frac{20}{3} \approx \underline{9}$ $\frac{15}{7} = 2\frac{1}{7}$ $\frac{20}{3} = 6\frac{2}{3}$

   $2 + 7 = 9$ $2\frac{1}{7} \approx 2$ $6\frac{2}{3} \approx 7$

   I renamed each fraction greater than 1 as a mixed number. Then, I rounded to the nearest whole number and added the rounded numbers.

Lesson 25:   Estimate sums and differences using benchmark numbers.   189

2. Ben's estimate for $8\frac{6}{10} - 3\frac{1}{4}$ was 6. Michelle's estimate was $5\frac{1}{2}$. Whose estimate do you think is closer to the actual difference? Explain.

   I think Michelle's estimate is closer to the actual difference. Ben rounded both numbers to the nearest whole number and then subtracted: $9 - 3 = 6$. Michelle rounded $8\frac{6}{10}$ to the nearest half, $8\frac{1}{2}$, and she rounded $3\frac{1}{4}$ to the nearest whole number. Then, she subtracted: $8\frac{1}{2} - 3 = 5\frac{1}{2}$. Since $8\frac{6}{10}$ is closer to $8\frac{1}{2}$ than 9, rounding it to the nearest half will give a closer estimate than rounding both numbers to the nearest whole number.

   > I can also draw number lines to show the actual difference, Ben's estimated difference, and Michelle's estimated difference. Because Ben rounded the total up and the part down, his estimated difference will be greater than the actual difference.

3. Use benchmark numbers or mental math to estimate the sum.

   $14\frac{3}{8} + 7\frac{7}{12} \approx 22$

   $14\frac{1}{2} + 7\frac{1}{2} = 21 + 1 = 22$

   > $\frac{3}{8}$ is 1 eighth less than $\frac{1}{2}$, and $\frac{7}{12}$ is 1 twelfth greater than $\frac{1}{2}$. I add the ones, and then I add the halves to get 22.

A STORY OF UNITS – TEKS EDITION　　　　　　　　　　　　Lesson 25 Homework　4•5

Name _____   Date _____

1. Estimate each sum or difference to the nearest half or whole number by rounding. Explain your estimate using words or a number line.

   a. $3\frac{1}{10} + 1\frac{3}{4} \approx$ _____

   b. $2\frac{9}{10} + 4\frac{4}{5} \approx$ _____

   c. $9\frac{9}{10} - 5\frac{1}{5} \approx$ _____

   d. $4\frac{1}{9} - 1\frac{1}{10} \approx$ _____

   e. $6\frac{3}{12} + 5\frac{1}{9} \approx$ _____

Lesson 25:   Estimate sums and differences using benchmark numbers.

2. Estimate each sum or difference to the nearest half or whole number by rounding. Explain your estimate using words or a number line.

   a. $\frac{16}{3} + \frac{17}{8} \approx$ _____

   b. $\frac{17}{3} - \frac{15}{4} \approx$ _____

   c. $\frac{57}{8} + \frac{26}{8} \approx$ _____

3. Gina's estimate for $7\frac{5}{8} - 2\frac{1}{2}$ was 5. Dominick's estimate was $5\frac{1}{2}$. Whose estimate do you think is closer to the actual difference? Explain.

4. Use benchmark numbers or mental math to estimate the sum or difference.

a. $10\frac{3}{4} + 12\frac{11}{12}$	b. $2\frac{7}{10} + 23\frac{3}{8}$
c. $15\frac{9}{12} - 8\frac{11}{12}$	d. $\frac{56}{7} - \frac{31}{8}$

1. Solve.

   $6\frac{2}{5} + \frac{3}{5} = 6\frac{5}{5} = 7$

   > I add using unit form. 6 ones 2 fifths + 3 fifths = 6 ones 5 fifths.
   > I know that $\frac{5}{5} = 1$, so $6 + 1 = 7$.

2. Complete the number sentence.

   $18 = 17\frac{3}{10} + \frac{7}{10}$

   > I know that $17 + 1 = 18$, so I need to find a fraction that equals 1 when added to $\frac{3}{10}$. $3 + 7 = 10$, so the fraction that completes the number sentence is 7 tenths.

3. Use a number bond and the arrow way to show how to make one. Solve.

   $3\frac{5}{8} + \frac{6}{8}$

   Number bond: $\frac{6}{8}$ decomposes into $\frac{3}{8}$ and $\frac{3}{8}$

   > I decompose $\frac{6}{8}$ into $\frac{3}{8}$ and $\frac{3}{8}$ because I know $3\frac{5}{8}$ needs $\frac{3}{8}$ to make the next whole number, 4.

   $3\frac{5}{8} \xrightarrow{+\frac{3}{8}} 4 \xrightarrow{+\frac{3}{8}} 4\frac{3}{8}$

   > The arrow way reminds me of making ten or making change from a dollar.

4. Solve.

   $\frac{7}{8} + 4\frac{6}{8}$

   $\frac{7}{8} + 4\frac{6}{8} = 4\frac{13}{8} = 5\frac{5}{8}$

   > I can add using any method that makes sense to me, like adding in unit form, using the arrow method, or adding to make the next 1, as shown below.
   >
   > $\frac{7}{8} + 4\frac{6}{8} = \frac{5}{8} + 5 = 5\frac{5}{8}$
   >
   > Number bond: $\frac{6}{8}$ decomposes into $\frac{5}{8}$ and $\frac{2}{8}$

Lesson 26: Add a mixed number and a fraction.

A STORY OF UNITS – TEKS EDITION   Lesson 26 Homework   4•5

Name _____   Date _____

1. Solve.

   a. $4\frac{1}{3} + \frac{1}{3}$

   b. $5\frac{1}{4} + \frac{2}{4}$

   c. $\frac{2}{6} + 3\frac{4}{6}$

   d. $\frac{5}{8} + 7\frac{3}{8}$

2. Complete the number sentences.

a. $3\frac{5}{6} +$ _____ $= 4$	b. $5\frac{3}{7} +$ _____ $= 6$
c. $5 = 4\frac{1}{8} +$ _____	d. $15 = 14\frac{4}{12} +$ _____

3. Draw a number bond and the arrow way to show how to make one. Solve.

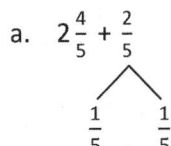

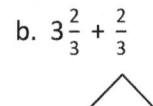

   a. $2\frac{4}{5} + \frac{2}{5}$

   (number bond: $\frac{2}{5}$ → $\frac{1}{5}$, $\frac{1}{5}$)

   b. $3\frac{2}{3} + \frac{2}{3}$

   c. $4\frac{4}{6} + \frac{5}{6}$

   $2\frac{4}{5} \xrightarrow{+\frac{1}{5}} 3 \xrightarrow{+\frac{1}{5}} 3\frac{1}{5}$

Lesson 26: Add a mixed number and a fraction.   195

4. Solve.

a.	$2\frac{3}{5} + \frac{3}{5}$	b.	$3\frac{6}{8} + \frac{4}{8}$
c.	$5\frac{4}{6} + \frac{3}{6}$	d.	$\frac{7}{10} + 6\frac{6}{10}$
e.	$\frac{5}{10} + 8\frac{9}{10}$	f.	$7\frac{8}{12} + \frac{11}{12}$
g.	$3\frac{90}{100} + \frac{58}{100}$	h.	$\frac{60}{100} + 14\frac{79}{100}$

5. To solve $4\frac{8}{10} + \frac{3}{10}$, Carmen thought, "$4\frac{8}{10} + \frac{2}{10} = 5$ and $5 + \frac{1}{10} = 5\frac{1}{10}$."
Benny thought, "$4\frac{8}{10} + \frac{3}{10} = 4\frac{11}{10} = 4 + \frac{10}{10} + \frac{1}{10} = 5\frac{1}{10}$." Explain why Carmen and Benny are both right.

A STORY OF UNITS – TEKS EDITION
Lesson 27 Homework Helper 4•5

1. Solve.

   $3\frac{1}{5} + 2\frac{4}{5}$

   $3\frac{1}{5} + 2\frac{4}{5} = 5 + \frac{5}{5} = 5 + 1 = 6$

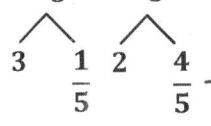

   Number bond: $3\frac{1}{5}$ decomposes into 3 and $\frac{1}{5}$; $2\frac{4}{5}$ decomposes into 2 and $\frac{4}{5}$.

   > I can add like units. 3 ones 1 fifth + 2 ones 4 fifths = 5 ones 5 fifths.

   > I can use number bonds to decompose the numbers into ones and fifths.

2. Solve. Use a number line to show your work.

   $1\frac{2}{3} + 3\frac{2}{3}$

   $1\frac{2}{3} + 3\frac{2}{3} = 4 + \frac{4}{3} = 5\frac{1}{3}$

   Number bond: $\frac{4}{3}$ decomposes into $\frac{3}{3}$ and $\frac{1}{3}$.

   Number line showing jumps of $+\frac{3}{3}$ and $+\frac{1}{3}$ from 4 to $5\frac{1}{3}$.

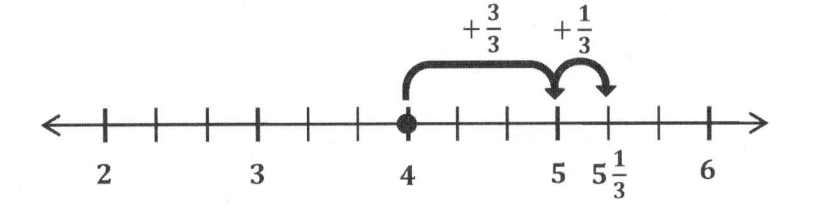

   > I add the ones and thirds. I decompose $\frac{4}{3}$ into 1 and $\frac{1}{3}$. $4 + 1 + \frac{1}{3} = 5\frac{1}{3}$

3. Solve. Use the arrow way to show how to make one.

   $4\frac{7}{12} + 3\frac{9}{12}$

   $4\frac{7}{12} + 3\frac{9}{12} = 7\frac{7}{12} + \frac{9}{12} = 8\frac{4}{12}$

   Number bond: $\frac{9}{12}$ decomposes into $\frac{5}{12}$ and $\frac{4}{12}$.

   $7\frac{7}{12} \xrightarrow{+\frac{5}{12}} 8 \xrightarrow{+\frac{4}{12}} 8\frac{4}{12}$

   > I use the arrow way to add $\frac{5}{12}$ and $7\frac{7}{12}$ to make the next whole number. Then, I add the other part of the number bond to get $8\frac{4}{12}$.

Lesson 27: Add mixed numbers.

Name _____ Date _____

1. Solve.

   a. $2\frac{1}{3} + 1\frac{2}{3} = 3 + \frac{3}{3} =$

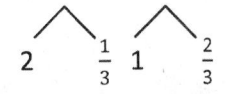

   (bond: 2 and $\frac{1}{3}$; 1 and $\frac{2}{3}$)

   b. $2\frac{2}{5} + 2\frac{2}{5}$

   c. $3\frac{3}{8} + 1\frac{5}{8}$

2. Solve. Use a number line to show your work.

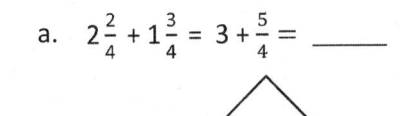

   a. $2\frac{2}{4} + 1\frac{3}{4} = 3 + \frac{5}{4} =$ _____

   (bond: $\frac{4}{4}$ and $\frac{1}{4}$)

   b. $3\frac{4}{6} + 2\frac{5}{6}$

   c. $1\frac{9}{12} + 1\frac{7}{12}$

Lesson 27: Add mixed numbers.

3. Solve. Use the arrow way to show how to make one.

   a. $2\frac{3}{4} + 1\frac{3}{4} = 3\frac{3}{4} + \frac{3}{4} =$

   $\frac{1}{4} \quad \frac{2}{4}$

   $3\frac{3}{4} \xrightarrow{+\frac{1}{4}} 4 \longrightarrow$

   b. $2\frac{7}{8} + 3\frac{4}{8}$

   c. $1\frac{7}{9} + 4\frac{5}{9}$

4. Solve. Use whichever method you prefer.

   a. $1\frac{4}{5} + 1\frac{3}{5}$

   b. $3\frac{8}{10} + 1\frac{5}{10}$

   c. $2\frac{5}{7} + 3\frac{6}{7}$

A STORY OF UNITS – TEKS EDITION

Lesson 28 Homework Helper   4•5

1. Subtract. Model with a number line or the arrow way.

   $4\frac{3}{5} - \frac{2}{5} = 4\frac{1}{5}$

   > I can subtract 2 fifths $\frac{1}{5}$ at a time or all at once.

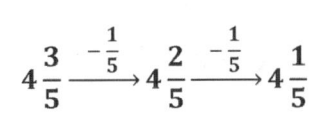

   $4\frac{3}{5} \xrightarrow{-\frac{1}{5}} 4\frac{2}{5} \xrightarrow{-\frac{1}{5}} 4\frac{1}{5}$

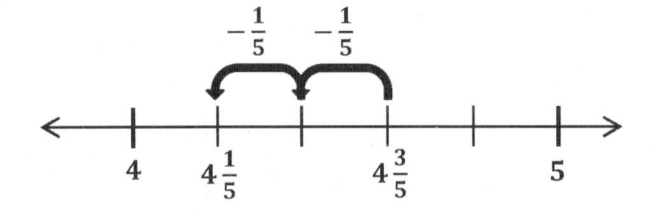

2. Use decomposition to subtract the fractions. Model with a number line or the arrow way.

   $6\frac{2}{6} - \frac{5}{6}$

   with number bond: $\frac{5}{6}$ decomposed into $\frac{2}{6}$ and $\frac{3}{6}$

   > I decompose $\frac{5}{6}$ into $\frac{2}{6}$ and $\frac{3}{6}$ so that I can subtract $\frac{2}{6}$ from $6\frac{2}{6}$ to get to a whole number.

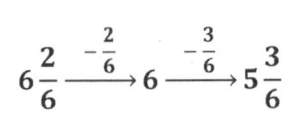

   $6\frac{2}{6} \xrightarrow{-\frac{2}{6}} 6 \xrightarrow{-\frac{3}{6}} 5\frac{3}{6}$

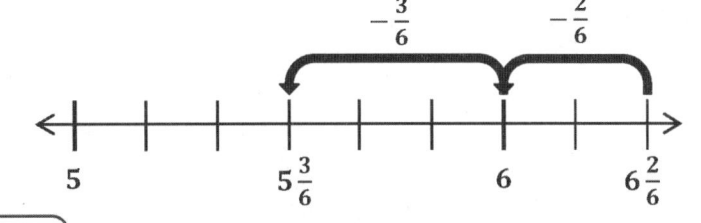

   > I subtract the other part of the number bond, $\frac{3}{6}$.

3. Decompose the total to subtract the fraction.

   $8\frac{2}{12} - \frac{9}{12}$

   > There aren't enough twelfths to subtract 9 twelfths, so I decompose the total to subtract $\frac{9}{12}$ from 1.

   $8\frac{2}{12} - \frac{9}{12} = 7\frac{2}{12} + \frac{3}{12} = 7\frac{5}{12}$

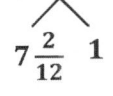

   number bond: $8\frac{2}{12}$ decomposed into $7\frac{2}{12}$ and 1

   > Once $\frac{9}{12}$ is subtracted, the remaining numbers are added together.

Lesson 28:   Subtract a fraction from a mixed number.

Name _____ Date _____

1. Subtract. Model with a number line or the arrow way.

   a. $6\frac{3}{5} - \frac{1}{5}$

   b. $4\frac{9}{12} - \frac{7}{12}$

   c. $7\frac{1}{4} - \frac{3}{4}$

   d. $8\frac{3}{8} - \frac{5}{8}$

2. Use decomposition to subtract the fractions. Model with a number line or the arrow way.

   a. $2\frac{2}{5} - \frac{4}{5}$

   $\frac{2}{5}$ $\frac{2}{5}$

   b. $2\frac{1}{3} - \frac{2}{3}$

   c. $4\frac{1}{6} - \frac{4}{6}$

   d. $3\frac{3}{6} - \frac{5}{6}$

e. $9\frac{3}{8} - \frac{7}{8}$

f. $7\frac{1}{10} - \frac{6}{10}$

g. $10\frac{1}{8} - \frac{5}{8}$

h. $9\frac{4}{12} - \frac{7}{12}$

i. $11\frac{3}{5} - \frac{4}{5}$

j. $17\frac{1}{9} - \frac{5}{9}$

3. Decompose the total to subtract the fractions.

a. $4\frac{1}{8} - \frac{3}{8} = 3\frac{1}{8} + \frac{5}{8} = 3\frac{6}{8}$

   $3\frac{1}{8}$ ／＼ 1

b. $5\frac{2}{5} - \frac{3}{5}$

c. $7\frac{1}{8} - \frac{3}{8}$

d. $3\frac{3}{9} - \frac{4}{9}$

e. $6\frac{3}{10} - \frac{7}{10}$

f. $2\frac{5}{9} - \frac{8}{9}$

Lesson 28: Subtract a fraction from a mixed number.

A STORY OF UNITS – TEKS EDITION

Lesson 29 Homework Helper 4•5

1. Write a related addition sentence. Subtract by counting on. Use a number line or the arrow way to help.

$6\frac{1}{4} - 2\frac{3}{4} = 3\frac{2}{4}$

> I add the numbers on top of the arrows to find the unknown addend.
> $\frac{1}{4} + 3 + \frac{1}{4} = 3\frac{2}{4}$

$2\frac{3}{4} + 3\frac{2}{4} = 6\frac{1}{4}$

$2\frac{3}{4} \xrightarrow{+\frac{1}{4}} 3 \xrightarrow{+3} 6 \xrightarrow{+\frac{1}{4}} 6\frac{1}{4}$

> I use the arrow way to count up to solve for the unknown in my addition sentence. I add $\frac{1}{4}$ to get to the next one, 3.

> I add 3 to get to 6.

> My final number needs to be $6\frac{1}{4}$, so I need to add 1 more fourth.

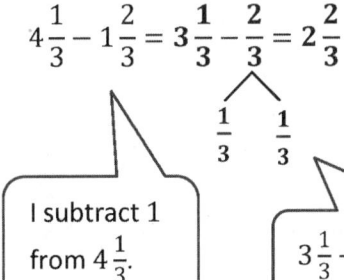

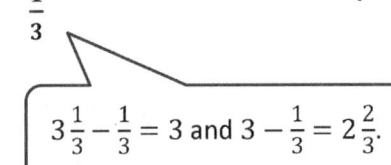

2. Subtract by decomposing the fractional part of the number you are subtracting. Use a number line or the arrow way to help you.

$4\frac{1}{3} - 1\frac{2}{3} = 3\frac{1}{3} - \frac{2}{3} = 2\frac{2}{3}$

$\frac{1}{3} \quad \frac{1}{3}$

> I subtract 1 from $4\frac{1}{3}$.

> $3\frac{1}{3} - \frac{1}{3} = 3$ and $3 - \frac{1}{3} = 2\frac{2}{3}$.

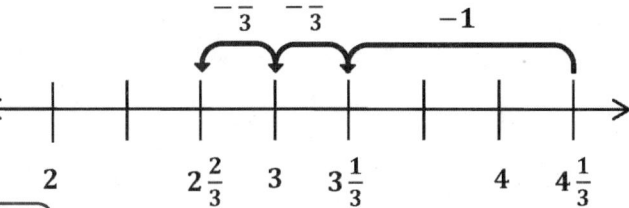

Number line showing $-\frac{1}{3}$, $-\frac{1}{3}$, -1 arrows from $4\frac{1}{3}$ back to $2\frac{2}{3}$, with marks at 2, $2\frac{2}{3}$, 3, $3\frac{1}{3}$, 4, $4\frac{1}{3}$.

Lesson 29: Subtract a mixed number from a mixed number.

207

3. Subtract by decomposing to take one out.

$7\frac{2}{10} - 5\frac{9}{10}$

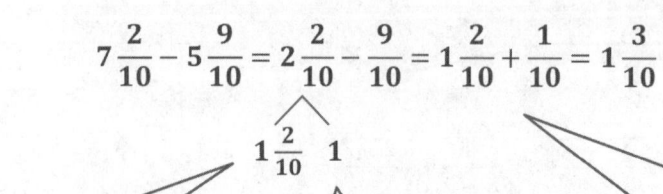

$$7\frac{2}{10} - 5\frac{9}{10} = 2\frac{2}{10} - \frac{9}{10} = 1\frac{2}{10} + \frac{1}{10} = 1\frac{3}{10}$$

Number bond under $2\frac{2}{10}$: $1\frac{2}{10}$ and 1.

- I decompose $2\frac{2}{10}$ to take 1 out.
- I subtract $1 - \frac{9}{10}$.
- I add the other part of the number bond, $1\frac{2}{10}$, to the difference of $1 - \frac{9}{10}$.

Name _____   Date _____

1. Write a related addition sentence. Subtract by counting on. Use a number line or the arrow way to help. The first one has been partially done for you.

   a. $3\frac{2}{5} - 1\frac{4}{5} =$ _____

   $1\frac{4}{5} +$ _____ $= 3\frac{2}{5}$

   b. $5\frac{3}{8} - 2\frac{5}{8}$

2. Subtract, as shown in Problem 2(a) below, by decomposing the fractional part of the number you are subtracting. Use a number line or the arrow way to help you.

   a. $4\frac{1}{5} - 1\frac{3}{5} = 3\frac{1}{5} - \frac{3}{5} = 2\frac{3}{5}$

   $\frac{1}{5} \quad \frac{2}{5}$

   b. $4\frac{1}{7} - 2\frac{4}{7}$

   c. $5\frac{5}{12} - 3\frac{8}{12}$

Lesson 29: Subtract a mixed number from a mixed number.

3. Subtract, as shown in 3(a) below, by decomposing to take one out.

   a. $5\frac{5}{8} - 2\frac{7}{8} = 3\frac{5}{8} - \frac{7}{8} =$

   (with number bond showing $3\frac{5}{8}$ decomposed into $2\frac{5}{8}$ and 1)

   b. $4\frac{3}{12} - 3\frac{8}{12}$

   c. $9\frac{1}{10} - 6\frac{9}{10}$

4. Solve using any strategy.

   a. $6\frac{1}{9} - 4\frac{3}{9}$

   b. $5\frac{3}{10} - 3\frac{6}{10}$

   c. $8\frac{7}{12} - 5\frac{9}{12}$

   d. $7\frac{4}{100} - 2\frac{92}{100}$

A STORY OF UNITS – TEKS EDITION

Lesson 30 Homework Helper   4•5

1. Subtract.

$$8\frac{2}{7} - \frac{6}{7} = 7\frac{9}{7} - \frac{6}{7} = 7\frac{3}{7}$$

$8\frac{2}{7}$ decomposed into 7 and $\frac{9}{7}$

> Now I have 9 sevenths, which is enough sevenths to subtract 6 sevenths.

> It's just like renaming 1 ten for 10 ones when subtracting whole numbers, except I rename 1 one for 7 sevenths.

2. Subtract the ones first.

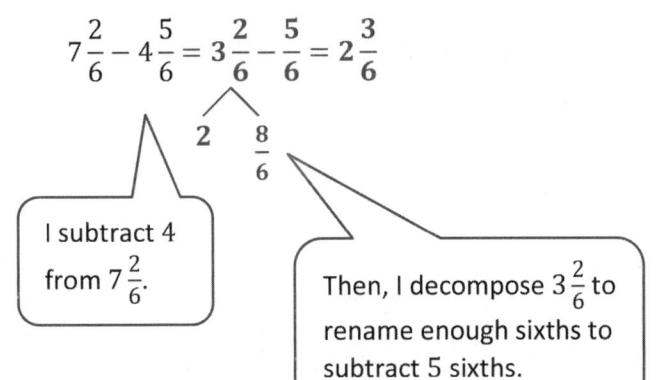

$$7\frac{2}{6} - 4\frac{5}{6} = 3\frac{2}{6} - \frac{5}{6} = 2\frac{3}{6}$$

$3\frac{2}{6}$ decomposed into 2 and $\frac{8}{6}$

> I subtract 4 from $7\frac{2}{6}$.

> Then, I decompose $3\frac{2}{6}$ to rename enough sixths to subtract 5 sixths.

$$7\frac{2}{6} \xrightarrow{-4} 3\frac{2}{6} \xrightarrow{-\frac{5}{6}} 2\frac{3}{6}$$

> I can show the same work with the arrow way.

Lesson 30:   Subtract mixed numbers.

Name _____   Date _____

1. Subtract.

   a. $5\frac{1}{4} - \frac{3}{4}$

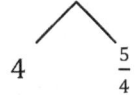

   (number bond: 4 and $\frac{5}{4}$)

   b. $6\frac{3}{8} - \frac{6}{8}$

   c. $7\frac{4}{6} - \frac{5}{6}$

2. Subtract the ones first.

   a. $4\frac{1}{5} - 1\frac{3}{5} = 3\frac{1}{5} - \frac{3}{5} = 2\frac{3}{5}$

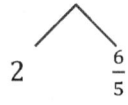

   (number bond: 2 and $\frac{6}{5}$)

   b. $4\frac{3}{6} - 2\frac{5}{6}$

Lesson 30: Subtract mixed numbers.

c. $8\frac{3}{8} - 2\frac{5}{8}$

d. $13\frac{3}{10} - 8\frac{7}{10}$

3. Solve using any strategy.

   a. $7\frac{3}{12} - 4\frac{9}{12}$

   b. $9\frac{6}{10} - 5\frac{8}{10}$

   c. $17\frac{2}{16} - 9\frac{7}{16}$

   d. $12\frac{5}{100} - 8\frac{94}{100}$

A STORY OF UNITS – TEKS EDITION

Lesson 31 Homework Helper 4•5

1. It takes $9\frac{2}{3}$ yards of yarn to make one baby blanket. Upik needs four times as much yarn to make four baby blankets. She already has 6 yards of yarn. How many more yards of yarn does Upik need to buy in order to make four baby blankets?

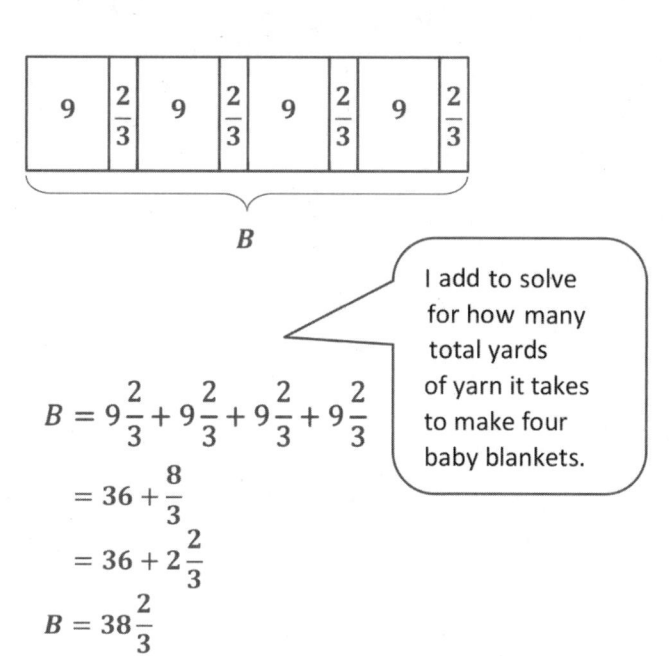

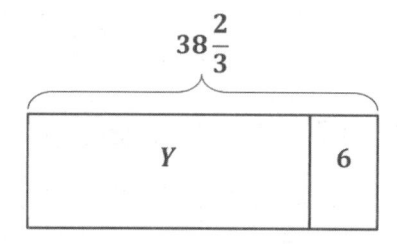

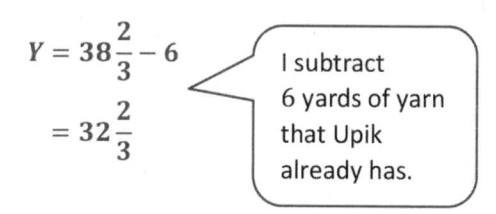

I add to solve for how many total yards of yarn it takes to make four baby blankets.

$$B = 9\frac{2}{3} + 9\frac{2}{3} + 9\frac{2}{3} + 9\frac{2}{3}$$
$$= 36 + \frac{8}{3}$$
$$= 36 + 2\frac{2}{3}$$
$$B = 38\frac{2}{3}$$

$$Y = 38\frac{2}{3} - 6$$
$$= 32\frac{2}{3}$$

I subtract 6 yards of yarn that Upik already has.

Upik needs to buy $32\frac{2}{3}$ more yards of yarn.

Lesson 31: Solve multiplicative comparison word problems involving fractions.

2. The caterpillar crawled $34\frac{2}{3}$ centimeters on Monday. He crawled 5 times as far on Tuesday. How far did he crawl in the two days?

> I use the strip diagram to find the most efficient way to solve. To solve for C, I find the value of 6 units.

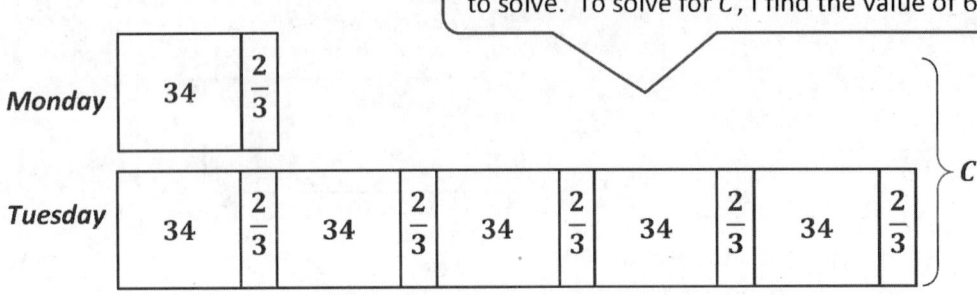

Monday: 34 | $\frac{2}{3}$

Tuesday: 34 | $\frac{2}{3}$ | 34 | $\frac{2}{3}$ | 34 | $\frac{2}{3}$ | 34 | $\frac{2}{3}$ | 34 | $\frac{2}{3}$ | 34 | $\frac{2}{3}$ } C

The caterpillar crawled 208 centimeters, or 2 meters 8 centimeters, on Monday and Tuesday.

$$C = 34\frac{2}{3} + 34\frac{2}{3} + 34\frac{2}{3} + 34\frac{2}{3} + 34\frac{2}{3} + 34\frac{2}{3}$$

$$C = 204 + \frac{12}{3}$$

$$C = 204 + 4$$

$$C = 208$$

Name _____ Date _____

Use the RDW process to solve.

1. Ground turkey is sold in packages of $2\frac{1}{2}$ pounds. Dawn bought eight times as much turkey that is sold in 1 package for her son's birthday party. How many pounds of ground turkey did Dawn buy?

2. Trevor's stack of books is $7\frac{7}{4}$ inches tall. Rick's stack is 3 times as tall. What is the difference in the heights of their stacks of books?

3. It takes $8\frac{3}{4}$ yards of fabric to make one quilt. Gail needs three times as much fabric to make three quilts. She already has two yards of fabric. How many more yards of fabric does Gail need to buy in order to make three quilts?

Lesson 31: Solve multiplicative comparison word problems involving fractions.

4. Cal made punch. He used $12\frac{3}{8}$ cups of juice and then added three times as much ginger ale. Then, he added 1 cup of lemonade. How many cups of punch did he recipe make?

5. Brandon drove $72\frac{7}{10}$ miles on Monday. He drove 3 times as far on Tuesday. How far did he drive in the two days?

6. Mrs. Reiser used $9\frac{8}{10}$ gallons of gas this week. Mr. Reiser used five times as much gas as Mrs. Reiser used this week. If Mr. Reiser pays $3 for each gallon of gas, how much did Mr. Reiser pay for gas this week?

Credits

Great Minds® has made every effort to obtain permission for the reprinting of all copyrighted material. If any owner of copyrighted material is not acknowledged herein, please contact Great Minds for proper acknowledgment in all future editions and reprints of this module.